Electronic Analog
Computer Primer

A Blaisdell Book in the Pure and Applied Sciences

CONSULTING EDITOR
Leon Lapidus, *Princeton University*

Electronic Analog Computer Primer

JAMES E. STICE

University of Arkansas

AND

BERNET S. SWANSON

Illinois Institute of Technology

BLAISDELL PUBLISHING COMPANY

A Division of Ginn and Company

NEW YORK · LONDON · TORONTO

FIRST EDITION, 1965

Copyright © 1965, by Blaisdell Publishing Company,
A Division of Ginn and Company.

All rights reserved.
Library of Congress Catalog Card Number: 65-18916
Printed in the United States of America

Preface

A LARGE BODY OF LITERATURE is available on the care and feeding of
analog computers, but when we first became interested in the field it
seemed that most of this material had been written for those with
a pretty solid background in electronics. After an initial period of
study, we began trying to solve some problems on our computer,
becoming more and more successful as we acquired understanding
and experience. Later when we had developed some proficiency in
the sport we found that we had accumulated quite a file of notes. It
occurred to us that these notes might be useful to others, and this
book was accordingly written.

Our aim was to present the fundamentals of analog computation
as simply as possible so that the reader who is not well grounded in
electronics, but who has at least a nodding acquaintance with
differential equations, can understand and use analog computers.
A review of circuit theory and electronics and the application of
these subjects to analog computers is included for those who may be
interested; those who are not may skip Chapter 2. Next the operations which can be performed with analog computers are examined.
Time and magnitude scaling are then presented and illustrated by
examples. A problem is stated, scaled, and programmed to show
the application of the techniques previously studied. Finally, four
types of commercially available computers are described in detail. It
is hoped that the novice, after reading this book, will be ready to try
his hand at the game.

One cannot hope to develop facility with analog computers simply by reading a book on the subject. Application should begin with simple problems, and if the reader cannot think of any right off, we have thoughtfully provided some interesting ones in Chapter 8, these being arranged in order of increasing complexity.

We are indebted to the National Science Foundation for Grants 12473 and 17773 which made this work possible. We are also sincerely grateful to Dr. Athanassios Costikas, formerly of the electrical engineering faculty of the Illinois Institute of Technology and now with the Greek Atomic Energy Commission. Dr. Costikas critically reviewed the material on circuit theory and electronics and gave valuable advice on technical accuracy and simplicity of presentation.

We further wish to acknowledge the contributions of the following individuals, who furnished information, illustrations, and suggestions: C. R. Moores (Applied Dynamics, Inc.), Paul Williams (Datronics Inc.), Rudolf F. Wagner (Donner Division of Systron-Donner Corp.), L. Arthur Hoyt and Edward J. Mangold (Electronic Associates, Inc.), and Bob Scowcroft and Earl F. Broihier (Heath Company).

JAMES E. STICE
Fayetteville, Arkansas

BERNET S. SWANSON
Chicago, Illinois

Contents

Electronic Analog
Computer Primer

I

Electronic Analog Computer Primer

The general-purpose electronic analog computer is one of several types of modern electronic equipment used for performing mathematical computations automatically. As a result of the cost of these various types of equipment, extensive computing facilities are currently found only in certain kinds of industries and in the larger colleges. Digital computers are much more numerous in these computer centers than general-purpose electronic analog computers of comparable cost. This is no doubt as it should be, since the digital machines can be used for a greater variety of calculations, such as bookkeeping, payroll, inventory control, records processing, statistical studies, and scientific and engineering design calculations.

The general-purpose analog computer, however, is particularly suited for certain kinds of calculations. Such a computer is mainly used for the solution of differential equations, and is therefore useful in the study of systems which can be described by a set of simultaneous differential equations. This is the reason for the wide application of analog computers in the study of automatic control systems; the equations which describe the system may be set up on the computer, and the resulting "model" of the real system may then be studied to see how the real system will behave. Analog computers are also widely used in the study of nonlinear differential equations, a field in which they have no equal.

1

★ Computer Classification

Computers are much in the news these days, and a lot of the news is so garbled and distorted that it is pretty hard for the average reader to separate the truth from the static. Some eager but misinformed journalists have dubbed the computers "thinking machines," and the resulting flood of half-truths and rumors would make H. G. Wells and Curt Siodmak rub their paws with glee. Accordingly, a brief discussion of several kinds of computers will be given to help the reader differentiate between them.

Digital computers are devices which deal in numbers only and which use addition as their basic function. A desk calculator adds the revolutions and partial revolutions of gears and displays the total number of revolutions of the various gears as a sum. The mileage register of an automobile speedometer is partly digital in its action; it counts the number of revolutions of the wheels, and by suitable gearing displays the total number of miles traveled. An electronic digital computer counts electrical pulses, and multiplies and divides by addition or subtraction. For instance, in multiplying 548 by 7357, the computer adds 7357 to itself 548 times (in considerably less than a second), and can produce an answer to almost any number of significant figures desired. Such a machine can also make logical decisions, in that it can compare two numbers to determine if one is larger than, smaller than, or equal to the other.

There are several types of analog computers. All of them relate the variables and parameters in a problem to variables and parameters in the analog model. Examples of direct analogs include wind tunnels (aeronautical and mechanical), network analyzers (electrical), process pilot plants (chemical), and model dams and model basins (hydraulic).

Indirect analog computers include nomographs (general), the slide rule (general), the general-purpose mechanical analog computers such as Dr. Vannevar Bush's Mark I calculator (the differential analyzer), and indirect electrical analog computers.

The indirect electronic analog computer is probably the most common of the indirect type. This type uses high-gain "operational" amplifiers to perform mathematical operations. This is the type of computer with which we will be concerned here, and when the term "analog computer" is used in the following pages, the reader will understand that the indirect electronic analog computer is meant.

Recently digital and analog computers have been combined to take advantage of the unique features of both machines. The resulting machine is the so-called "hybrid" computer, and the use of these computers will no doubt increase as their capabilities become better known.

Incidentally, the question of whether computers can "think" has been vigorously debated, and one of the conclusions which has emerged from this argument seems to be that we do not really know what "thinking" is.† It is certain that present-day computers cannot do anything which they have not been programmed to do. As a matter of fact, they must be told exactly what to do in solving a given problem, down to the smallest detail. Since they are entirely literal, they follow their programmed instructions explicitly. If the instructions are not detailed enough, or are incorrect, the machine will either just sit there and look at the operator, or it will develop electronic indigestion and belch out nonsense.

Also, present-day computers cannot make value judgments in subjective areas such as the social and moral fields, art, and the like (and one wonders whether they will ever be able to do so). Much research is under way to develop computers which are capable of rudimentary thought, but there are no machines which are capable of thinking at this time.

★ **Advantages of Analog Computers**

The choice of a particular kind of computer for a specific kind of calculation depends upon several factors, including the nature of the problem and the degree of precision required in the solution. The analog computer has certain features which are not found in digital computers.

Probably the chief advantage in analog computation is that the operator retains a "feel" for his problem. The twisting of a po-

---

†See, for example, Ulric Meisser's article, "The Imitation of Man by Machine," *Science*, **139** (January 18, 1963), 193–197, and the resulting letter in *Science*, **140** (April 12, 1963), 212–218.

tentiometer on the computer represents, in a very real sense, the variation of a controller setting or the changing of a coefficient in the process which is under study. Thus, the analog computer set-up becomes a working model, or simulation, of the real physical problem, and the operator finds himself thinking of one block of computer components as a control valve and another block as a heat exchanger. Changes in settings of computer components thus become meaningful in terms of the real process, and the results of these changes can be interpreted immediately in the same terms. The operator can "think as he goes," and if interesting side-avenues open up, these can be immediately explored.

Time is also capable of variation in analog computation. The choice of time scale is limited only by the speed of the read-out equipment being used; thus a problem may be speeded up so that it is many times faster than the actual process, or slowed down so that the simulated process occurs more slowly than the real process. The actual solution time for a problem is quite short. Even quite complicated problems rarely require minutes, and several seconds is much more common.

Before discussing accuracy and precision, these terms require definition. The word *accuracy* as used here denotes how closely a solution conforms to fact. *Precision* of a solution is an indication of the sharpness of definition. As an example, consider the value of e, the base of natural logarithms. The value 2.718282 is more precise than 2.718, but both values are accurate.

Analog computers generally yield results having three, or at most, four significant figures. However, for many engineering purposes, three significant figures will be adequate, since the original data will be no better. Unfortunately, many people seem to think that a solution which contains ten significant figures is highly accurate, even though some of the input data have only two or three significant figures.

It is not difficult to learn how to program an analog computer. Of course the more difficult problems require a correspondingly greater amount of experience and knowledge on the part of the programmer, but persons with technological backgrounds can pick up the fundamentals of the analog computing art quickly. The development of greater skill is then only a matter of practice and continued study.

★ Applications of Analog Computers

Analog computers can solve ordinary linear and nonlinear differential equations with either constant or variable coefficients, algebraic equations, and partial differential equations. Since this is intended only as an introduction to the field, the solution of algebraic and partial differential equations will not be discussed here. However, those who wish to investigate them are referred to Jackson [1] or to Rogers and Connolly [2].

Aside from the use of the analog computer as an equation-solving machine, it is particularly useful as a device for simulating systems. Perhaps the widest use of the computer has been in this field, with applications in the chemical process industries, missile and high-speed aircraft programs, and instrument development. Synthesis of proposed control systems or the analysis of existing systems by means of analog simulation techniques give rapid and reliable information about optimum control settings and sluggish or unstable responses. It is hoped that the following discussion and the laboratory exercises will awaken the reader to the possibilities of the computer.

★ Requirements for Computing Amplifiers

Amplifiers which are to be used for computing purposes must meet several requirements, among which are

1. High open-loop gain.
2. High input impedance.
3. Constant closed-loop gain for all frequencies from direct current to several thousand cycles per second.
4. A phase shift of 180 degrees between input voltage and output voltage.
5. Linearity over a wide operating region.
6. Zero output voltage when there is no input signal.

Probably some readers are not familiar with all the terms used above. It is our opinion that it is not necessary for the beginner to understand the inner workings of the machine in order to learn how to program it for the solution of problems of moderate complexity. On the other hand, those who wish to become adept at the art, and who intend to use the computer for the investigation of difficult problems, will sooner or later be obliged to learn something about the electronics of the computer components.

Chapter 2 provides a review of alternating current circuit theory and basic electronics theory which are fundamental to an understanding of the operational amplifiers—the heart of an analog computer. Chapter 3 discusses the operational amplifier from the standpoints of gain, phase shift, drift, and linearity. Those readers who have some training in electronics should find these two chapters helpful, especially if their background has accumulated some flecks of rust. The beginner may wish to skip Chapters 2 and 3 for the time being and return to them when he finds he needs the information.

II

Review of Circuit Theory and Amplifiers

★ **Phase Shift**

In electrical circuits, it is found that when a sinusoidal voltage is applied across a linear, passive component such as a resistor, capacitor, or inductor, a sinusoidal current flows in the component. The instantaneous voltage is represented by the equation

$$e = E_m \sin (\omega t + \theta), \tag{1}$$

where e is the instantaneous voltage, E_m is the maximum value of the voltage, ωt is the angular displacement in radians, and θ is the initial phase angle in radians, measured from some arbitrary point in time.

The instantaneous current resulting from this applied voltage is represented by

$$i = I_m \sin (\omega t + \Phi), \tag{2}$$

where i is the instantaneous current in amperes, I_m is the maximum value of the current, and Φ is the initial phase angle in radians, measured from the same point in time as θ in Equation (1).

Figure 2.1 shows a plot of a voltage and its associated current as a function of time.

In Figure 2.1 the arbitrary zero point in time was chosen to be the point at which the voltage wave crosses the horizontal axis while

7

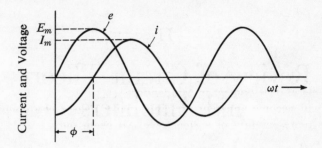

FIGURE 2.1. *Instantaneous voltage and current in a circuit component.*

changing from a negative to a positive value. Then the initial phase angle for voltage is 0°, or,

$$e = E_m \sin (\omega t + \theta) = E_m \sin \omega t. \tag{3}$$

With respect to the same zero point in time, the current has a phase angle of $-90°$ (or $+270°$), which is $-\frac{\pi}{2}$ radians. Then

$$i = I_m \sin (\omega t + \Phi) = I_m \sin \left(\omega t - \frac{\pi}{2} \right). \tag{4}$$

The current is said to *lag* the voltage by 90°, or the voltage *leads* the current by 90°. There is a phase shift of 90° between the two waveforms.

★ Representation of Sinusoidal Voltages and Currents by Phasors

In alternating current (ac) circuit theory, a knowledge of instantaneous values of voltages and currents is required. However, mathematical manipulation of sine waves of different amplitudes and phase angles often involves a formidable amount of labor if trigonometric expressions are used for currents and voltages. In order to simplify the solution of circuit problems, Steinmetz originated the idea of representing a sinusoidally-varying quantity by a rotating line segment called a *phasor*. By definition, this line segment has a constant magnitude which is equal to the maximum value of the sinusoidally-varying quantity. Also, the phasor is positioned so that its vertical projection represents the instantaneous value of the sine wave at some chosen time, usually at time $t = 0$. Finally, the line segment rotates about the origin in a counterclockwise direction with an angular velocity equal to that of the sinusoidal quantity which it represents. Since the phasor concept is an important one in ac circuit theory, it will be developed in some detail here, following the general development in Middendorf [3].

It will become apparent presently that a phasor is a complex-plane representation of a sine wave. To begin our development, consider a stationary vector of magnitude E and direction θ plotted in the complex plane (see Figure 2.2). The vector **E** can be represented by the equation

$$\mathbf{E} = a + jb, \tag{5}$$

where a is the horizontal projection of **E** measured along the real axis, and b is the vertical projection of **E** measured along the imaginary axis. The symbol j precedes a quantity to be measured along the imaginary axis. The term "imaginary" was used by the early mathematicians, probably because it means the opposite of "real." This was an unfortunate choice of term, since many beginning students of mathematics infer that the imaginary quantities do not exist, although in fact, there is nothing imaginary about them. It is helpful to look upon j as an operator which rotates the quantity it precedes by 90° in the counterclockwise direction. Then j^2 rotates the quantity by 180°, j^3 by 270°, and so on. The **E** is printed in boldface type to denote the fact that the voltage is a complex quantity, having both real and imaginary parts, and hereafter all complex quantities will be so represented.

From Figure 2.2, it can be seen that

$$a = E \cos \theta \tag{6}$$

$$b = E \sin \theta. \tag{7}$$

Upon combination with Equation (5),

$$\mathbf{E} = E \cos \theta + jE \sin \theta = E(\cos \theta + j \sin \theta). \tag{8}$$

One of the elementary relationships of complex variable theory is

$$e^{j\theta} = \cos \theta + j \sin \theta. \tag{9}$$

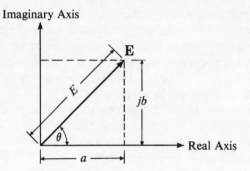

FIGURE 2.2.   *Complex plane representation of vector* **E**.

By using this relationship, Equation (8) becomes

$$\mathbf{E} = Ee^{j\theta}. \tag{10}$$

Upon referring to Figure 2.2, the magnitude of **E** is, by the Pythagorean Theorem:

$$E = \sqrt{a^2 + b^2}. \tag{11}$$

From elementary trigonometry, the angle θ is defined to be

$$\theta = \tan^{-1} \frac{b}{a}. \tag{12}$$

The vector **E** is now defined by Equation (10), with magnitude and direction given by Equations (11) and (12).

The phasor we are seeking is not a vector; it is a *rotating line segment*, with an angular velocity of ω radians per second. Thus, if the vector can be caused to rotate with the desired velocity, then the phasor is obtained. The rotation can be included by multiplying Equation (10) by a rotational operator having an angle which increases with time. Then the phasor is:

$$\mathbf{E} = Ee^{j\theta}e^{j\omega t} = Ee^{j(\omega t + \theta)} \tag{13}$$

$$= E[\cos (\omega t + \theta) + j \sin (\omega t + \theta)]. \tag{14}$$

Now the object of all this manipulation is to be able to express the instantaneous value of a sine wave at any instant of time. The imaginary portion of the phasor is the sinusoidal function desired, and represents a sinusoidal voltage having a maximum value E_m, an angular velocity ω, and a phase angle of θ radians at time $t = 0$. This is the quantity described by Equation (1), or

$$e = E_m \sin (\omega t + \theta). \tag{1}$$

Then the imaginary part of the phasor (Equation 14) represents the sinusoidal voltage of Equation (1). Figure 2.3 shows this sine wave, together with the corresponding phasor representation.

The figure shows that, at any instant of time, the vertical projection of the phasor is equal to the instantaneous value of the sinusoidally-varying voltage which it represents. For example, at $t = 0$, the instantaneous value of the voltage sine wave is

$$e = E_m \sin (\omega t + \theta) = E_m \sin \theta. \tag{15}$$

At the same instant of time, since the length of the phasor is E_m, the vertical projection of the phasor is $E_m \sin \theta$, which agrees with Equation (15). It should be realized that the phasor is not *equal* to the sine wave, but it permits expression of the necessary information about the sine wave for many types of calculations.

At the beginning of this section, the phasor was defined to have a length equal to the maximum value of the sinusoidally-varying quantity. However, an ammeter or voltmeter does not indicate the maximum value, but an effective value called the *root mean square*, or rms value. (The reader who is not familiar with rms values should consult any elementary text on ac circuits.) In order to make

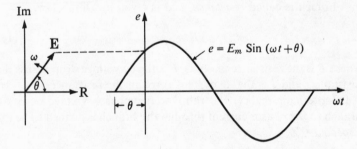

FIGURE 2.3. *Sine wave of voltage represented by a phasor and by the trigonometric function.*

the phasor concept more useful, the length of the phasor has, by agreement, been set equal to the rms value rather than the maximum value. The rms value of a voltage sine wave is equal to $E_m/\sqrt{2}$. In the rest of the text, rms values are presented by capital letters, as E.

The notation which has been agreed upon for representation of a sinusoidal voltage as a phasor is (polar form)

$$\mathbf{E} = E\underline{/\theta}, \tag{16}$$

where E is the rms value of the voltage, and θ is the initial phase angle. Similarly, a current phasor is represented by

$$\mathbf{I} = I\underline{/\Phi}. \tag{17}$$

The phasor of Equation (16) can also be expressed in rectangular form as $\mathbf{E} = E_x + jE_y$. The expression of currents and voltages as phasors allows one to perform the following mathematical operations on sinusoidal quantities with far less labor than would be the case if the quantities were expressed trigonometrically: addition, subtraction, multiplication, division, raising to powers, extraction of roots, and obtaining the logarithm. The reader who is not familiar with the algebra of complex numbers will find a review of the subject, and electrical engineering examples, in any good text on elementary ac circuit theory.

★ Impedance

In direct current (dc) circuit theory, the ratio of voltage to current in a branch is called *resistance*, and is given by Ohm's law,

$$R = \frac{E}{I}, \tag{18}$$

where R is the resistance in ohms, E is the dc voltage drop across the resistance, and I is the dc current through the resistance.

In ac circuit theory, the ratio of the phasor voltage across a branch to the phasor current through the branch is defined to be the *impedance*, $\mathbf{Z}$,

$$\mathbf{Z} = \frac{\mathbf{E}}{\mathbf{I}} = \frac{E\underline{/\theta}}{I\underline{/\Phi}}. \tag{19}$$

Since the impedance is the ratio of two complex numbers, it is itself a complex number. Then it can be represented in rectangular form by

$$\mathbf{Z} = R + jX, \tag{20}$$

where $\mathbf{Z}$ is the complex value of the impedance in ohms, R is the resistance in ohms (real component of impedance), and X is the reactance in ohms (imaginary component of impedance). Reactance may be of two types, inductive or capacitive. For a pure inductor, $X = \omega L$, where L is the inductance in henrys. For a pure capacitor, $X = -1/\omega C$, where C is the capacitance in farads.

Equation (19) defines impedance for sinusoidal voltages and currents only, since phasors apply only to sinusoidal quantities. However, the concept of impedance may be generalized to include voltage and current waveforms which are arbitrary functions of time. This involves writing the differential equation of the circuit involved and then taking the Laplace transform of this differential equation. The ratio of the voltage transform to the current transform is the transform of the impedance (called the Z transform), and the inverse transform of the Z transform is the generalized impedance of the circuit. The method is applicable to any waveform whatever. Since a knowledge of Laplace transform techniques is not presupposed here, the method will not be enlarged upon, but the interested reader is referred to van Valkenburg [4] for very readable discussions of the application of Laplace transforms to electrical circuits and the use of the Z transform.

To summarize, impedance is the ratio of the voltage across a branch to the current through the branch. For sinusoidal voltages and currents the impedance is the ratio of phasor voltage to phasor current, and for nonsinusoidal voltages and currents, the impedance is the inverse Laplace transform of the Z transform. Impedance is a complex quantity, having both magnitude and direction, and in complex notation (rectangular coordinates) it consists of a real part (resistance) and an imaginary part (reactance).

★ **Amplifiers and Gain**

In general, an amplifier is a device which produces an output that is a magnified form of the input. Only electronic amplifiers will be

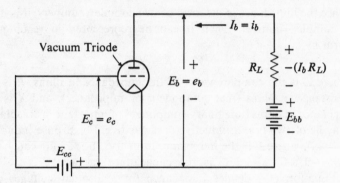

FIGURE 2.4.   *Simple triode amplifier, no-signal condition.*

discussed here, and the development given follows the material in Gray's *Applied Electronics* [5].

Figure 2.4 shows a simple triode amplifier with a resistance load under quiescent conditions (no signal applied to the triode grid). In the figure, E_{cc} is the grid bias supply voltage (direct current) which always maintains the grid at a potential lower than the cathode potential, so that no current flows in the grid circuit. E_{bb} is the plate (anode) voltage supply (also direct current) which maintains the plate at a higher potential than that of the cathode. The voltage drop across the tube (difference between the plate potential and the cathode potential) is E_b. The voltage drop across load resistor R_L is $I_b R_L$, with polarity defined as shown in the diagram. The current flowing in the plate circuit is I_b, and the direction of this current is as shown. This is the "conventional" current, which flows in a direction opposite to the flow of electrons. Since the electron flow in the tube is from cathode to plate, the direction of the flow of conventional current is from plate to cathode.

It is necessary to define the symbols for the various currents and voltages in the amplifier of Figure 2.4 in order to discuss the operation clearly. The following symbols and definitions are those adopted by the Institute of Radio Engineers [6].

I_b = value of the current through the external circuit toward the plate, when there is no time-varying component of grid voltage.

E_b = value of the voltage rise from cathode to plate, when there is no time-varying component of grid voltage.

E_c = value of the voltage rise from cathode to grid, when there is no time-varying component of grid voltage.

i_b = instantaneous total current through the external circuit toward the plate.

e_b = instantaneous total voltage rise from cathode to plate.

e_c = instantaneous total voltage rise from cathode to grid.

i_p = instantaneous value of the time-varying component of current through the external circuit toward the plate.

e_g = instantaneous value of the time-varying component of the grid-signal voltage.

e_p = instantaneous value of the time-varying component of the voltage rise from cathode to plate.

For the simple triode amplifier of Figure 2.4, a little study will show that the following relationships exist under no-signal conditions:

$$e_g = 0 \text{ (no grid signal applied)}$$

$$e_p = 0$$

$$i_p = 0$$

$$e_c = E_c$$

$$e_b = E_b$$

$$i_b = I_b.$$

When a time-varying signal is applied to the grid, the above relationships change. Figure 2.5 shows the same amplifier with a varying grid signal applied. In Figure 2.5 all of the voltages and currents now contain a varying component in addition to the no-

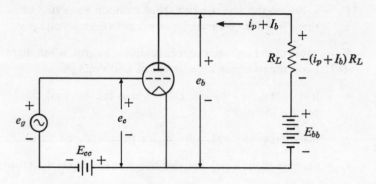

FIGURE 2.5.   *Simple triode amplifier with grid signal applied.*

signal (steady-state) component, as a result of the application of the grid signal e_g. The relationships become:

$$e_g = e_g$$

$$e_c = E_{cc} + e_g$$

$$e_b = E_b + e_p$$

$$e_p = -i_p R_L$$

$$i_b = I_b + i_p.$$

Consider that the amplitude of the grid signal e_g is small, so that the operation of the amplifier is linear. Also, the frequency of e_g is low enough for the effect of tube interelectrode capacitances to be negligible. Then it can be shown [7] that the circuit of Figure 2.5 is

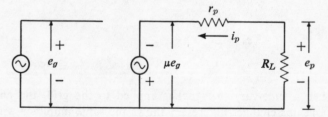

FIGURE 2.6.   *Voltage-source equivalent circuit for simple triode amplifier with resistance load.*

equivalent, for purposes of analysis, to the circuit of Figure 2.6. Figure 2.6 is called the voltage-source equivalent circuit of the amplifier shown in Figure 2.5.

In Figure 2.6 the triode has been replaced by a resistance r_p (the tube plate resistance) in series with an ideal voltage source μe_g (with polarity as shown), where μ is the tube amplification factor. No steady-state (dc) voltages or currents appear in the equivalent circuit, since it applies only to incremental changes in voltage and current caused by incremental changes in the grid signal, e_g.

The voltage gain of the circuit in Figure 2.6 will now be derived. The term *gain* is the amount of amplification obtained from an amplifier, and *voltage gain* is defined to be the ratio of the instantaneous value of the varying component of the output voltage rise to the corresponding instantaneous value of the varying component of the input grid-signal voltage rise. The symbol for gain is **A**.

By Kirchhoff's voltage law, the algebraic sum of the instantaneous values of voltage drops around any closed path of a circuit is equal to zero. By applying this law to the plate circuit of Figure 2.6, and summing in a counterclockwise direction we obtain

$$i_p R_L + i_p r_p - \mu e_g = 0 \tag{21}$$

$$i_p(R_L + r_p) = \mu e_g. \tag{22}$$

Also, because of the direction of current i_p, and the defined direction of polarity for voltage e_p,

$$e_p = -i_p R_L \tag{23}$$

$$i_p = -\frac{e_p}{R_L}. \tag{24}$$

By substituting Equation (24) into Equation (22):

$$-\frac{e_p}{R_L}(R_L + r_p) = \mu e_g. \tag{25}$$

Upon rearranging,

$$\frac{e_p}{e_g} = -\frac{\mu R_L}{R_L + r_p} = \text{Gain} = \mathbf{A}. \tag{26}$$

Equation (26) applies to any input signal-voltage waveform; e_g need be neither sinusoidal nor periodic. If the input is a sinusoidal voltage, then the equation may be written in other forms. For instance,

$$\frac{\mathbf{E}_p}{\mathbf{E}_g} = -\frac{\mu R_L}{R_L + r_p} = \text{Voltage Gain} = \mathbf{A}. \qquad (27)$$

In a simple triode amplifier such as the one shown in Figure 2.5, suppose that a sinusoidal input signal e_g is applied. As the signal voltage becomes more positive, the triode grid becomes more positive, and the tube current increases. This causes the voltage drop across the load resistor, which is equal to $i_p R_L$, to increase also. However, the output voltage is $e_p = -i_p R_L$, so that the output voltage *decreases* as i_p increases. Thus, as e_g goes positive, e_p goes negative, and vice versa. Then there is a phase shift of 180° between e_g and e_p.

Equation (27) is the gain expression for a simple triode amplifier with a sinusoidal input voltage and a pure resistance load. The amplification factor for the tube, μ, is a real number, and so are the values of resistances R_L and r_p. Then the gain is a *negative real number*, having a magnitude of $\mu R_L / (R_L + r_p)$, and a phase shift of 180° between input and output voltages.

If the amplifier has a load which is a complex impedance rather than the pure resistance shown in Figure 2.5, then the gain is no longer a real number, but becomes a complex number. If the complex impedance load is designated by $\mathbf{Z}_L$, then Equation (27) becomes

$$\mathbf{A} = \frac{\mathbf{E}_p}{\mathbf{E}_g} = -\frac{\mu \mathbf{Z}_L}{\mathbf{Z}_L + r_p}. \qquad (28)$$

Suppose, for the purpose of illustration, that the load is a pure resistance in parallel with a pure capacitance, as shown in Figure 2.7.

In the circuit shown, both branches have the same voltage drop, $\mathbf{V}$, across them. Also, by Kirchhoff's current law, the sum of the branch currents $\mathbf{I}_1$ and $\mathbf{I}_2$ must be equal to the current $\mathbf{I}$ entering the branch, or

$$\mathbf{I} = \mathbf{I}_1 + \mathbf{I}_2. \qquad (29)$$

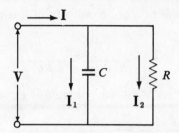

FIGURE 2.7.   *Load consisting of resistor and capacitor in parallel.*

The impedance of the capacitor is

$$\mathbf{Z}_c = 0 - j\frac{1}{\omega C}. \tag{30}$$

The impedance of the resistor is

$$\mathbf{Z}_R = R + j0. \tag{31}$$

Since, in general, $\mathbf{V} = \mathbf{I}\mathbf{Z}_L$, then

$$\mathbf{I}_1 = \frac{\mathbf{V}}{\mathbf{Z}_c} = \frac{\mathbf{V}}{-j\dfrac{1}{\omega C}} = \frac{\mathbf{V}\omega C}{-j}\cdot\frac{j}{j} = j\mathbf{V}\omega C. \tag{32}$$

Similarly,

$$\mathbf{I}_2 = \frac{\mathbf{V}}{\mathbf{Z}_R} = \frac{\mathbf{V}}{R}. \tag{33}$$

The combination of Equations (29), (32), and (33) yields

$$\mathbf{I} = \mathbf{I}_1 + \mathbf{I}_2 = j\mathbf{V}\omega C + \frac{\mathbf{V}}{R} = \mathbf{V}\left[\frac{1}{R} + j\omega C\right] \tag{34}$$

$$\mathbf{Z}_L = \frac{\mathbf{V}}{\mathbf{I}} = \frac{\mathbf{V}}{\mathbf{V}\left(\dfrac{1}{R} + j\omega C\right)} = \frac{R}{1 + j\omega RC}. \tag{35}$$

By substituting Equation (35) into Equation (28) we obtain

$$\mathbf{A} = -\frac{\mu\left(\dfrac{R}{1 + j\omega RC}\right)}{\dfrac{R}{1 + j\omega RC} + r_p}. \tag{36}$$

Equation (36) will be more meaningful if it is put into the form $A = R + jX$.

$$A = \frac{-\mu R}{(R + r_p) + j\omega R C r_p}. \tag{37}$$

Upon rationalization of the denominator of Equation (37):

$$
\begin{aligned}
A &= \frac{-\mu R}{(R + r_p) + j\omega R C r_p} \cdot \frac{(R + r_p) - j\omega R C r_p}{(R + r_p) - j\omega R C r_p} \\
&= \frac{-\mu R(R + r_p) + j\mu\omega R^2 C r_p}{(R + r_p)^2 + \omega^2 R^2 C^2 r_p^2} \\
&= \frac{-\mu R(R + r_p)}{(R + r_p)^2 + \omega^2 R^2 C^2 r_p^2} + j\frac{\mu\omega R^2 C r_p}{(R + r_p)^2 + \omega^2 R^2 C^2 r_p^2}.
\end{aligned}
\tag{38}
$$

Equation (38) expresses the voltage gain of the simple triode amplifier as a complex number (rectangular form). For sinusoidal signals, the term ω in the equations is equal to $2\pi f$, where f is the frequency of the signal in cycles per second.† Equation (38) shows that the voltage gain decreases as the frequency of the grid signal becomes large. Also, since the real part of the gain term is negative, while the imaginary part is positive, the phase angle is in the second quadrant. Thus, as ω increases from zero to infinity, the phase varies from $-180°$ to $-270°$, or from $+180°$ to $+90°$.

The value of μ, the tube amplification factor, is also variable. Tube characteristics vary during warming-up, under changes in ambient temperature, and with normal aging. Further, two tubes of precisely the same make and type will not have identical characteristics, so that gain changes result when tubes are replaced.

The material in the last several pages has been presented to demonstrate the fact that the voltage gain and the phase shift of the simple triode amplifier are not constants, but are subject to several sources of variation. It will now be shown that the use of feedback will make the gain a constant for the over-all feedback amplifier over a considerable range of frequencies.

---

†For nonsinusoidal signals, the generalized impedance transform must be used, and the equivalent expression to Equation (38) for nonsinusoidal signals will not be developed here.

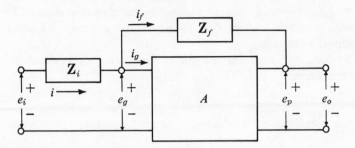

FIGURE 2.8.   *Feedback amplifier.*

★ Amplifier with Negative Feedback

In the preceding section, it was shown that the gain of a simple triode amplifier with a complex impedance load varies with the frequency. Also, the phase shift is not 180° at all frequencies. In order to remedy this situation, use is made of negative, or degenerative, feedback. A feedback amplifier is depicted in Figure 2.8.

The rectangle marked A in Figure 2.8 is an amplifier such as we have been discussing with gain $\mathbf{A}$ (a complex number). The input signal e_i is fed through impedance $\mathbf{Z}_i$ to the grid of the input tube of amplifier A. The output voltage e_p (which is identical with e_0) acts on the input signal through impedance $\mathbf{Z}_f$ to produce the resultant grid signal e_g.

The voltage feedback through impedance $\mathbf{Z}_f$ is of opposite polarity to the voltage e_g, whence the name *negative* feedback. The use of negative feedback makes the gain of the feedback amplifier somewhat independent of the gain of the internal amplifier, and if the gain of the internal amplifier is made high enough, the gain and phase angle of the feedback amplifier become constants over a range of frequencies. In order that this point may be well understood, the gain expression for the feedback amplifier of Figure 2.8 will be derived.

Assume that e_i is positive at the moment being considered. Then the direction of the current i is as shown, since e_g is less than e_i, and current always flows from a higher to a lower potential. Also, e_g is more positive than e_p (remember that if e_i is positive, then e_g is positive; e_p is negative, then e_g is at a higher potential than e_p). Therefore, current i_f flows in the direction shown. The direction of grid current i_g is unknown at this time, and will be assumed as shown.

By Kirchhoff's current law, the algebraic sum of all currents at a node must equal zero. Then

$$i = i_f + i_g. \tag{39}$$

Upon using complex values for current, Equation (39) becomes

$$\mathbf{I} = \mathbf{I}_f + \mathbf{I}_g. \tag{40}$$

We will now assume that the grid current i_g is small enough to be ignored. This is an important assumption, and depends upon the fact that the input impedance of amplifier A is large enough (several megohms) for the small grid voltage e_g to cause only a negligible grid current to flow. Then,

$$\mathbf{I} = \mathbf{I}_f. \tag{41}$$

In order to make this development entirely general, complex quantities will be used throughout. In the input circuit, since voltage drop is equal to the product of current times impedance,

$$\mathbf{E}_i - \mathbf{E}_g = \mathbf{I}\mathbf{Z}_i \tag{42}$$

$$\mathbf{I} = \frac{\mathbf{E}_i - \mathbf{E}_g}{\mathbf{Z}_i}. \tag{43}$$

Similarly, for the feedback circuit,

$$\mathbf{I}_f = \frac{\mathbf{E}_g - \mathbf{E}_p}{\mathbf{Z}_f}. \tag{44}$$

Since $\mathbf{E}_p$ is identical to $\mathbf{E}_0$, Equation (44) may be written

$$\mathbf{I}_f = \frac{\mathbf{E}_g - \mathbf{E}_0}{\mathbf{Z}_f}. \tag{45}$$

Substitution of Equations (43) and (45) into Equation (41) yields,

$$\frac{\mathbf{E}_i - \mathbf{E}_g}{\mathbf{Z}_i} = \frac{\mathbf{E}_g - \mathbf{E}_0}{\mathbf{Z}_f}. \tag{46}$$

Since the generalized gain term we are seeking will be in terms of E_i and E_0, it is necessary to express E_g in terms of one or the other. Equation (28) gives the desired relationship,

$$A = \frac{E_p}{E_g} = \frac{E_0}{E_g}.$$

Then

$$E_g = \frac{E_0}{A}. \tag{47}$$

After making this substitution in Equation (46),

$$\frac{Z_f}{Z_i}\left(E_i - \frac{E_0}{A}\right) = \frac{E_0}{A} - E_0 \tag{48}$$

$$\frac{Z_f}{Z_i}E_i = \frac{E_0}{A} - E_0 + \frac{Z_f}{Z_i}\cdot\frac{E_0}{A} = E_0\left(\frac{1}{A} + \frac{1}{A}\cdot\frac{Z_f}{Z_i} - 1\right). \tag{49}$$

Upon rearranging Equation (49),

$$G = \frac{E_0}{E_i} = \frac{\dfrac{Z_f}{Z_i}}{\dfrac{1}{A}\left(1 + \dfrac{Z_f}{Z_i}\right) - 1}. \tag{50}$$

Equation (50) expresses the voltage gain of the feedback amplifier as a function of the complex impedances Z_f and Z_i and the complex voltage gain of the internal amplifier, A. Only one assumption was made in deriving the equation, namely that the grid current i_g was negligible. Equation (50) is completely general for any kind of input or feedback impedance, and for any complex voltage gain, A. The equation will give both the magnitude and the phase angle of the voltage gain of the feedback amplifier.

For practical feedback amplifiers, Equation (50) can be greatly simplified. If the gain of the internal amplifier is a sufficiently large quantity, then $1/A$ is very small, and Equation (50) reduces to

$$G = -\frac{Z_f}{Z_i}. \qquad \text{for high gain internal amplifier} \tag{51}$$

Let us substitute numbers into Equations (50) and (51) to convince the skeptic. Suppose that the magnitude of the gain of the internal amplifier is 50,000 and phase shift is 180°. Then A equals $-50,000 + j0$. Suppose also that the input and feedback impedances are one megohm resistors, so that $\mathbf{Z}_f = \mathbf{Z}_i = 1,000,000 + j0$. Equation (51) gives a voltage gain of exactly -1.00000 for the feedback amplifier. By using Equation (50),

$$\mathbf{G} = \cfrac{1}{\cfrac{2}{-50,000} - 1} = -\frac{50,000}{50,002} = -0.99996.$$

Thus, Equation (50) gives a gain magnitude of 0.99996 with a phase angle of 180°, and Equation (51) gives a gain magnitude of 1.00000 with the same phase angle. The latter equation gives a gain which is about 0.00004 higher than is obtained from the more complicated equation, and this is a negligible error. Equation (51) may be considered to be a satisfactory expression for the gain of the feedback amplifier, provided the gain $\mathbf{A}$ is high enough and the grid current i_g is negligible. The use of feedback has thus made the magnitude of the voltage gain constant. A word of caution— Equation (51) indicates that the gain of the feedback amplifier is independent of the gain of the internal amplifier, and is dependent only upon the values of the input and feedback impedances. This is an astonishing result, and is the basis for the use of the operational amplifier in analog computers. However, this constancy of the closed-loop gain does not hold as the frequency is increased without limit, and we shall see in the next chapter that as the frequency continues to increase the gain of the feedback amplifier begins to fall. In the range of usable frequencies, however, the voltage gain of the feedback amplifier is represented by Equation (51).

Two different types of amplifiers, as well as their associated voltage gains, have been under discussion. To make reference to them less cumbersome, they will be assigned descriptive titles. The amplifier which has no feedback path from its output terminal back to its input terminal has been called the internal amplifier. Its gain will be called *open-loop gain*, because there is no feedback path, or loop. The open-loop gain has been designated $\mathbf{A}$. The amplifier which does have a feedback path from its output terminal back to the input terminal (see Figure 2.8) has been called the feedback amplifier. The gain of this amplifier has been designated $\mathbf{G}$, and this gain will be called *closed-loop gain*, because there is a feedback path, or the feedback loop is closed.

III

The Operational Amplifier

In the preceding review of electronics, some of the characteristics of open-loop and closed-loop amplifiers were discussed. The amplifiers of an analog computer are high-gain dc amplifiers, and when impedances are placed in the input and feedback positions, the amplifiers become feedback amplifiers of the type shown in Figure 2.8. The closed-loop gain of these amplifiers in the usable range of frequencies is expressed by

$$G = -\frac{Z_f}{Z_i},\tag{51}$$

where G is the gain of the closed-loop amplifier in volts per volt, Z_f is the value of the feedback impedance in ohms, and Z_i is the value of the input impedance in ohms. Since the feedback amplifiers can perform mathematical operations, they are called operational amplifiers.

Some of the requirements for analog computer amplifiers have already been mentioned; now they will be discussed in somewhat greater detail.

★ **The Internal Amplifier**

OPEN-LOOP GAIN

The internal amplifier must have a high open-loop gain, in order that the closed-loop gain of the feedback amplifier will be a constant over a substantial frequency range (see Equations 50 and 51). Ragazzini *et al.* [8] believe the open-loop gain should be at least 5000, and gains of 10^3 to 10^8 are in use.

Gains of this magnitude are not obtained from a single-stage amplifier. Instead, multistage amplifiers are used, with the output voltage of the first stage becoming the input voltage to the second stage, and so on. For reasons which will be discussed in the next section, an odd number of stages is generally employed, and three stages is the most common arrangement. For instance, suppose each stage has an open-loop gain of 40. Then the over-all open-loop gain for a three-stage amplifier would be 40 × 40 × 40, or 64,000. Although this illustration is oversimplified, it will give an idea of the way in which large gains can be obtained from multistage amplifiers.

180° PHASE SHIFT FOR OVER-ALL AMPLIFIER

It is desirable to have an odd number of stages in the feedback amplifier because this is the easiest way in which the 180° phase shift between input voltage and output voltage can be achieved. One stage of amplification gives 180° phase shift, but the gain of such an amplifier is not high enough for acceptable accuracy in computation. The addition of a second stage of amplification gives another 180° phase shift so the total phase shift is 360°. Feedback of the output signal from the second stage to the input signal to the first stage will result in *addition* of the two signals, since they are in phase with each other. This is termed positive feedback, since the two signals add, and the arrangement will ultimately result in oscillation. Oscillation is an unstable situation characterized by the existence of an arbitrary voltage at the amplifier output terminals even though the input voltage is zero, and is clearly to be avoided.

The addition of a third stage of amplification will add still another 180° phase shift, so that the total phase angle is now 540°, which is equivalent to 180°. Then the output voltage of Stage 3 is 180° out of phase with the input voltage to Stage 1, as desired, and this condition will exist whenever an odd number of stages is used.

It should be mentioned that it is not essential that an odd number of stages be used in the internal amplifier. The reader should realize from the discussion of the complex impedance load shown in Figure 2.7 that an amplifier can be designed to have almost any phase shift desired, depending upon the nature of the load impedance of each stage. Thus, it is quite possible to provide the desired gain and 180° phase shift with four stages. However, resistive loads are normally used in computing amplifiers, and three stages of amplification are commonly used.

The reader should also realize that the phase shift of the internal amplifier is 180° only for low frequency input signals, and that the phase shift varies as the frequency increases (see Equation 38, and the attending discussion). The use of negative feedback bails us out again, however, and the phase angle of the feedback amplifier remains at 180° up to frequencies considerably higher than those at which the phase shift of the internal amplifier begins to depart from 180°. This will be discussed further in the section on phase shift of the feedback amplifier.

GRID CURRENT

As indicated in the discussion of Equation (40) it is undesirable to have current flowing in the grid of the input tube of the internal amplifier. The practical way to insure a negligible grid current is to select a tube which has a sufficiently small grid current. Some presently available triodes have grid currents as low as 10^{-10} to 10^{-11} ampere [9].

CIRCUIT DIAGRAMS OF THE INTERNAL AMPLIFIER

When a voltage amplifier is composed of several stages, the output of one stage must obviously be introduced into the input of the following stage. If a capacitor is connected between the two stages, a dc input voltage will cause no corresponding output voltage because a capacitor "blocks" dc current. Capacitor coupling is commonly used in ac amplifiers, since it is desired to remove dc components of signal voltages, and amplify only the ac components.

The internal amplifier of an operational amplifier is a dc voltage amplifier, which means that capacitors are not used to couple the stages together. As a result, a dc input voltage gives a nonzero output voltage, and the amplifier amplifies input signals with frequencies from 0 cycles per second up.

No effort will be made here to discuss amplifier design. However, there are many published circuit diagrams, with accompanying discussions, which the interested reader may wish to see.†

★ **The Feedback Amplifier**

GAIN

As discussed previously in the section dealing with the electronics review, the gain of the feedback amplifier, for practical purposes, is given by:

$$G = -\frac{Z_f}{Z_i}. \tag{51}$$

The comment was made that Equation (51) was applicable throughout the frequency range of interest. Perhaps that statement should be paraphrased to say that the frequency of interest should not be outside the range where Equation (51) is applicable. At any rate, it is desirable to know how the gain of the closed-loop amplifier varies with frequency, so that the frequency range for which Equation (51) applies is known. For complete information on the gain of any amplifier, a frequency response plot must be prepared.

A *frequency response plot*, also called the gain curve, is a plot

†Ragazzini, J. R., R. H. Randall, and F. A. Russell. "Analysis of Problems in Dynamics by Electronic Circuits," *Proc. IRE* **35** (May, 1947) 444–452.
Wass, C. A. A. *Introduction to Electronic Analog Computers.* New York: Pergamon Press, 1955. Pp. 64–87.
Korn, G. A., and T. M. Korn. *Electronic Analog Computers*, 2d ed. New York: McGraw-Hill Book Co., 1956. Pp. 190–250.

of the logarithm of the voltage gain as ordinate versus the log-arithm of the frequency as abscissa. To obtain this plot, one needs a sinusoidal signal generator and a voltmeter. A sine wave of voltage of given frequency and small amplitude is fed into the amplifier as the input signal. The input voltage and the output voltage are measured, and the ratio of output voltage to input voltage is the magnitude of the voltage gain at the frequency used. The frequency of the input signal is then varied, and a new output voltage is obtained. This procedure is repeated until the frequency band has been covered in which the gain is high enough to be of interest. The data are then used to prepare the frequency response plot.

There are several ways in which the gain may be expressed in the frequency response plot. The easiest is the numerical value of the ratio of the output voltage to the input voltage, and this method is frequently used. However, electrical engineers are in the habit of expressing voltage gain in decibels. This is probably because amplifiers were first used to amplify electrical signals for conversion into sound, and the human ear responds to stimuli on a logarithmic scale.

The decibel (abbreviated "db") is a power ratio, and is defined to be [10]

$$\text{Number of decibels by which } P_2 \text{ exceeds } P_1 = 10 \log_{10}\frac{P_2}{P_1}. \qquad (52)$$

When two voltages E_1 and E_2 are applied to the same (or equal) resistive loads, the power is proportional to the square of E, so

$$\text{Number of decibels by which } E_2 \text{ exceeds } E_1 = 10 \log_{10}\left(\frac{E_2}{E_1}\right)^2 = 20 \log_{10}\frac{E_2}{E_1}. \qquad (53)$$

Equation (53) thus defines the voltage gain in decibels.

Consider the situation where a given amplifier has an input voltage of magnitude E_1 at frequency f_1, giving resultant output voltage E_2. With the same input voltage E_1, but at a different frequency f_2, the output voltage becomes E_2'. Then,

$$\frac{P_2}{P_1} = \left(\frac{E_2'}{E_2}\right)^2 = \left(\frac{E_2'/E_1}{E_2/E_1}\right)^2 = \left(\frac{A'}{A}\right)^2, \qquad (54)$$

where A' and A are magnitudes only. Then we can write

$$\text{Number of decibels by which } A' \text{ exceeds } A = 10 \log_{10}\left(\frac{A'}{A}\right)^2 = 20 \log_{10}\frac{A'}{A} \cdot \quad (55)$$

The foregoing analysis assumes that the amplifier load is a pure resistance, and thus does not vary as the frequency is changed. In practice, the loads of most operational amplifiers are resistances, but there may be associated tube and wiring capacitances (which act in parallel with the resistive load) which have an effect at higher frequencies.

Equation (55) expresses the *relative voltage gain* in decibels. Gain A is chosen at some arbitrary frequency, and all gains A' at other frequencies are referred to this gain. When gain A' is higher than gain A, Equation (55) gives a positive value, and the voltage gain is said to be "so many decibels up" from the reference gain. When gain A' is lower than gain A, then Equation (55) gives a negative value, and the voltage gain is said to be "so many decibels down" from the reference value.

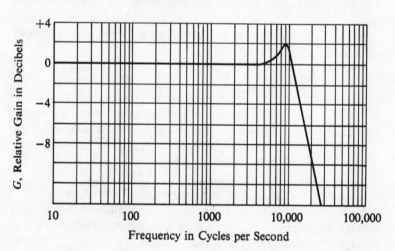

FIGURE 3.1. *Frequency response curve for Heathkit ES-201 dc amplifier with one megohm input and feedback resistors (By permission of the Heath Company, Subsidiary of Daystrom, Inc.)*

Equation (55) is written in terms of the open-loop gain, A, but it can be readily expressed in terms of the closed-loop gain, G.

$$\text{Number of decibels by which} \atop G' \text{ exceeds } G = 20 \log_{10} \frac{G'}{G}. \qquad (56)$$

Figure 3.1 shows the frequency response curve for the operational amplifier of the Heathkit Group C analog computer, with one megohm input and feedback resistors [11]. The gain curve is "flat" from 1 cps to about 4000 cps. The gain is up two db at 9000 cps and down three db at about 14,000 cps. The reference voltage gain G could have been chosen at any frequency from 1 to 4000 cps, but a mid-range frequency is normally chosen, say about 100 cps.

The hump in the gain curve between 5000 and 10,000 cps is due to a slight resonance in the amplifier. It was mentioned earlier that the loads of most operational amplifiers are resistances, but there are also capacitances associated with the electrodes in a vacuum tube, particularly with triodes. These capacitances are called inter-electrode capacitances. In addition, there are capacitances and stray inductances between the various wires in the circuit. The plate-to-cathode inter-electrode capacitance and the stray wiring capacitance are in parallel with the resistive load, as shown in Figure 2.7. At low frequencies, the capacitive reactance is very large (remember that $X_c = -1/\omega C$, with C in farads), and the capacitive branch acts like an open circuit. In the 5000 to 10,000 cps band, the resistance-capacitance load resonates with the stray inductances, causing the hump in the gain curve. Beyond 10,000 cps, the resonant effect vanishes, the inductive capacitive reactance begins to dominate, and the gain falls.

Figure 3.1 reveals that, as far as gain is concerned, Equation (51) is applicable for any input frequency between 1 cps and about 4000 cps. The actual usable frequency band is still not known, however, because the variation of phase shift with frequency has not been explored. This will be done in the next section.

The effect of the magnitude of the open-loop gain of the internal amplifier shows up dramatically in the frequency response plot. The open-loop gain of the amplifier shown in Figure 3.1 is

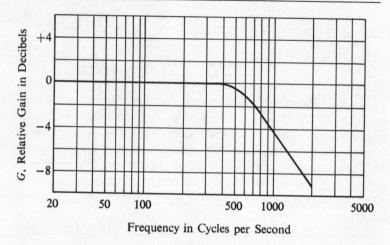

FIGURE 3.2. *Frequency response curve for amplifier of Heathkit model EC-1 educational analog computer, with one megohm input and feedback resistors (By permission of the Heath Company, Subsidiary of Daystrom, Inc.)*

30,000–50,000. Figure 3.2 shows the frequency response plot for the feedback amplifier of the Heathkit Model EC-1 Educational Analog Computer, with one megohm input and feedback resistors [12]. The open-loop gain of this amplifier is 1000, and the gain curve begins to fall off at about 400 cps, and is down three db at 850 cps. There is no hump in this curve, because the resonant frequency of the load was not reached. For the EC-1 amplifiers, Equation (51) is applicable only up to about 400 cps. Thus the lower open-loop gain of the amplifier of Figure 3.2 causes the amplifier to be usable over a much smaller range of frequencies than the amplifier of Figure 3.1.

As far as frequency limitations are concerned then, the accuracy of the Heathkit EC-1 computer will begin to be affected at frequencies above about 400 cps, and the accuracy of the Heathkit Group C computer (which uses the EC-201 amplifiers) is impaired above about 4000 cps. Thus, a computer input having a frequency up to 400 cps could be used with the EC-1 computer for a problem which is scaled in real time (see Chapter 5 for a discussion of time scaling). If the problem is scaled so that the solution is speeded up by a factor of 100, however, the maximum *problem* frequency is limited to 400/100, or four cps.

Another point — there are many types of forcing functions besides sinusoids. It is a happy circumstance that any function can be represented by an infinite series of sine or cosine functions. A step function or square wave is often used to force an analog simulation because the step function is easy to apply and there are standard techniques for analyzing the response to such an input. A step function is the most severe test that can be applied, however, because many harmonics are required to produce it. The higher harmonics may exceed the frequency response of the amplifiers being used, and yet the response of the real system to these harmonics may be important. The problem is further complicated if the analog model is time-scaled to speed up the solution. The frequency response of the amplifiers being used is an important consideration in such cases.

The Heathkit amplifiers which have been discussed here are admittedly limited to work at fairly low frequencies. This is not a criticism, since these computer kits are inexpensive and extended frequency response costs money; the Heathkit computers do very nicely on a variety of problems where flat frequency response over wide bandwidths is not required. Operational amplifiers which have flat frequency response up to 50,000 to 200,000 cps can be obtained from other manufacturers, but one of course pays more for the privilege of possessing them. Incidentally, it is difficult to obtain frequency response diagrams from manufacturers (the Heath Company being a notable exception), but this sort of information can be obtained from the salesman if one is sufficiently insistent and patient.

PHASE SHIFT

In the discussion of characteristics of the internal amplifier, the desirability of maintaining a phase shift of 180° between the input and output voltages was discussed. This phase shift is not difficult to obtain at low frequencies, but it becomes more difficult to maintain as the frequency rises.

Here again, the inter-electrode and stray wiring capacitances are the culprits. With low frequencies, the capacitive reactance is very large, and the load acts essentially like a pure resistance. Thus, the phase shift is 180°. As the frequency increases, the capacitive reactance decreases, and current begins to pass through the capacitive branch, at which time the phase shift begins to be affected (see Equation 38). If the frequency is allowed to go high enough, the phase angle may shift as much as 90° away from the 180° desired.

The use of negative feedback stabilizes this situation, just as it stabilizes the voltage gain. If the gain of the internal amplifier is high enough, the phase shift of the feedback amplifier will be small, even if the phase shift of the internal amplifier is appreciable. According to Wass [13], even if the phase shift of the internal amplifier is as much as 90° away from the desired 180°, the phase shift between input and output voltages will be less than 0.1°, provided the magnitude of the open-loop gain is a few thousand and normal closed-loop gains are used.

Perhaps some numbers will make this point clearer. Suppose that the magnitude of the open-loop gain is 50,000, and the phase shift is 90° away from 180°, at $+90°$. Then in rectangular form $A = 0 + j50,000$. Assume that the closed-loop gain is 10, with Z_f a one megohm resistor and Z_i a 100,000 ohm resistor. Then $Z_f = 1,000,000 + j0$, and $Z_i = 100,000 + j0$. Upon substituting these values into Equation (50),

$$G = \frac{\dfrac{1,000,000}{100,000}}{\dfrac{1}{j50,000}\left(1 + \dfrac{1,000,000}{100,000}\right) - 1} = \frac{10}{\dfrac{11}{j50,000} - 1} = \frac{10(j50,000)}{11 - j50,000}.$$

By rationalizing the denominator,

$$G = \frac{j500,000}{11 - j50,000} \cdot \frac{11 + j50,000}{11 + j50,000} = \frac{j5,500,000 - 25,000,000,000}{121 + 2,500,000,000}.$$

The 121 in the denominator is negligible in comparison with the 2,500,000,000, and will be dropped. Then,

$$G = -\frac{25,000,000,000}{2,500,000,000} + j\frac{5,500,000}{2,500,000,000} = -10 + j0.0022.$$

The magnitude of the gain is equal to the square root of $10^2 + (0.0022)^2$ (see Equation 12). This is essentially 10. The phase angle is equal to $\tan^{-1} 0.0022/-10 = \tan^{-1} -0.00022$ (see Equation 13). This angle is in the second quadrant, since the real part is negative and the imaginary part is positive. Then the angle is $+179°$ $59'$. The complex gain is then

$$G = 10\underline{/+179° \ 59'}.$$

Thus it is seen that a large variation in phase angle in the internal amplifier made a change of less than one minute in the phase shift of the feedback amplifier. This is not true at all frequencies, since there comes a time when the phase shift drifts away from 180°, even with feedback. However, there is a considerable range of frequencies for which the phase shift remains at 180° even when the phase shift of the internal amplifier is varying, and designing the amplifier to have a phase shift close to 180° extends this frequency range.

An investigation of the phase shift as frequency increases is desirable in order to determine the range of frequencies for which the phase shift remains at 180°. A plot of phase shift on a linear scale versus the logarithm of the frequency as abscissa is called the *phase characteristic,* and is the companion to the frequency response plot. The data for the phase characteristic can be taken at the same time the frequency response data are taken. For low frequencies, a Servoscope may be used with good accuracy. Also, a two-channel recorder gives good results within its frequency limitations. For all frequencies a cathode-ray oscilloscope may be used, the phase angle being measured from the Lissajous figure projected upon the scope screen. This method is approximate only, but gives results which are accurate to within 5 percent.

Figure 3.3 shows the phase characteristic of the ES-201 dc amplifier (operational amplifier of the Heathkit Group C computer), with one megohm input and feedback resistors [11]. The curve is flat to 3000 cps, and then begins to fall off. No phase characteristic plot is available for the Heathkit EC-1 amplifier.

The usable frequency range for the Heathkit ES-201 operational amplifier can be determined by studying Figures 3.1 and 3.3. The

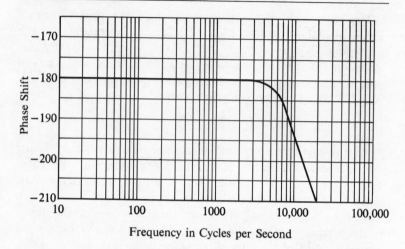

FIGURE 3.3   *Phase characteristic plot for Heathkit ES-201 dc amplifier with one megohm input and feedback resistors (By permission of the Heath Company, Subsidiary of Daystrom, Inc.)*

gain curve is flat to about 4000 cps (see Figure 3.1). The phase shift is constant at 180° out to a frequency of about 3000 cps (see Figure 3.3). Therefore, 3000 cps is about the top usable frequency.

It should be mentioned that the magnitudes of the input and feedback resistances have an effect on the usable frequency range. The closed-loop gain of the amplifiers used in obtaining the data for Figures 3.1, 3.2, and 3.3 was 1.0, and this gain was obtained by using one megohm input and feedback resistors. If 100,000 ohm resistors are used, the same closed-loop gain is obtained, but the results are somewhat different. The gain curve is flat to about 4000 cps, as before, but the phase shift begins to depart from 180° at around 1400 cps. Thus, the usable frequency range is about 1400 cps for 100,000 ohm resistors, and about 3000 cps with one megohm resistors, even though the closed-loop gains are the same.

The frequency at which phase shift becomes troublesome is also a function of the number of amplifiers in the computing circuit, and thus varies from problem to problem. The gain curve and the phase characteristic curve of the amplifiers being used give a good idea of the upper limit of frequency which may be used, but they may not be available, and they do not show the effect of the number of amplifiers being used. If it is necessary that the upper frequency limit be known fairly accurately, the operator can determine this reasonably well by running a problem at increasing frequencies. The solutions to the problem will begin to diverge when the frequency exceeds the top usable frequency.

DRIFT IN COMPUTING AMPLIFIERS

One of the biggest problems in the design of amplifiers for computing use is *drift*. It is obviously desirable to obtain zero output voltage from a computing amplifier when the input voltage is zero, since $E_0 = GE_i$ must be satisfied when $E_i = 0$. If this is not the case, then the amplifier is producing an output with no corresponding input. As a result, when an input signal is applied, the output voltage will be the sum of the amplified signal plus the output obtained with no signal, and an error has been introduced.

Some computing amplifiers are provided with a control which allows manual balancing of the amplifier. To balance, the input terminals are short-circuited, which sets the input voltage to zero; then the aforementioned balance control (actually a variable bias resistor in the cathode circuit of the input tube) is adjusted to set the output voltage to zero. As time passes, it will be noted that the output voltage will slowly depart from zero again, and this is the condition known as *drift*. It has several causes, including variation in vacuum-tube and filament (heater) supply voltages, changes in tube characteristics (resulting from aging or temperature variation), and changes in resistance values with age and temperature.

These causes of drift can be minimized by careful design of circuits and use of high-quality components, but the drift can never be eliminated in this way. With manual balancing, the operator must balance amplifiers from time to time, and especially before the start of each computer run. To eliminate this chore, many manufacturers have resorted to some kind of drift-correction scheme which automatically balances the amplifiers.

The most common automatic balancing circuits are the so-called *chopper stabilized* circuits, which utilize a synchronous vibrator (high-speed relay) to short-circuit the input terminals and simultaneously sample the voltage at the grid of the input tube. With the input terminals short-circuited, the only voltage on the grid is the drift voltage. The output of the chopper relay is a square wave, which is amplified by an auxiliary ac amplifier, reversed in sign, then rectified and filtered (smoothed). The smoothed wave is fed back to the grid of the input tube where it cancels the drift voltage, since it is approximately equal in magnitude and opposite in polarity to the drift voltage. Thus, the stabilizing circuit continually monitors the drift voltage and strives to reduce it to zero. Korn and Korn [14] report the following representative drift figures for high-quality chopper stabilized amplifiers: average drift over an eight-hour period, referred to input, is less than 20 to 200 microvolts.

The addition of automatic balancing circuits makes the computer amplifier package more expensive, but there are some other advantages to the use of the drift-correction circuits. The use of the auxiliary a-c amplifier increases the open-loop gain of the internal amplifier, results in better frequency response for the feedback amplifier, and allows the use of power supplies which are not as carefully regulated. The interested reader may wish to delve deeper into automatic balancing circuits, and Johnson [15] has the most readable discussion, together with a circuit diagram of the Reeves REAC amplifier. Korn and Korn [16] also discuss the subject, and give circuit diagrams of the RCA amplifier, the RAND amplifier, the Electronic Associates, Inc. PACE amplifier, and the Goodyear GEDA amplifier. Wass [17] also gives a good discussion, and gives the circuit diagram of the Elliott Bros. TRIDAC amplifier.

One other trouble, which acts very much like drift, is caused by the presence of a grid current in the input tube. When the input terminals are short-circuited, grid current will still flow in Z_{li}, causing a nonzero potential at the grid. The balancing of the amplifier will compensate for the voltage due to grid current, but the problem is better handled by choosing an input tube which has a very small grid current.

LINEARITY

In a preceding section, the variation of closed-loop gain with frequency was discussed. There is another source of variation of the closed-loop gain which involves the magnitude of the output voltage.

As the magnitude of the input signal voltage rises, the output voltage also increases in magnitude, and there should be a linear relationship between the two, that is,

$$G = \frac{E_0}{E_i} = -\frac{Z_f}{Z_i}. \tag{51}$$

In accordance with what has already been said, if the frequency of the input signal is chosen in the band where the gain curve is flat, then the gain is fixed by the ratio of the feedback and input impedances. This is true only up to a point, and some qualification is required.

The fact is that the output voltage of any real amplifier is limited, and the relationship between input voltage and output voltage is *not* linear throughout the entire range of output voltages. However, there is a range of output voltages for which amplifier operation is linear, or in other words, a plot of input voltage versus output voltage is a straight line. This range of output voltages is called the *operating range* of the amplifier. Outside of this range, the closed-loop gain of the amplifier is different from the **G** predicted by Equation (51), even though the frequency used is in the band where the gain curve and the phase characteristic curve are flat. This nonlinearity in the relationship between input and output voltages is called *amplitude distortion*, and it is nearly always accompanied by *intermodulation distortion*. The latter is revealed by the appearance of harmonic frequencies in the output voltage which were not present in the input voltage; these extraneous harmonics are termed *noise*.

Obviously, the wise and crafty practitioner wants no part of this type of nonlinearity in his computer solutions. The operating range for computer amplifiers is always specified, and commonly covers the range from −100 volts to +100 volts (transistorized computer amplifiers have smaller operating ranges, on the order of -10 volts to $+10$ volts). Within the operating range, amplifier operation is linear. Indicator lights are generally built into the output circuits of the individual amplifiers, and these become illuminated when the output voltage reaches the limit of the operating range. If one of these lights comes on in an amplifier which is in use, the operator knows that the amplifier has gone out of the linear range of operation. This is unavoidable in problems whose solutions go to infinity with time, but in other problems, a reduction in input voltages will prevent output voltages from going outside of the operating range. This topic will be discussed in Chapter 6, which deals with magnitude scaling.

IV

Mathematical Operations Performed with Operational Amplifiers

★ **Symbols for Operational Amplifiers**

An operational amplifier is a three-terminal network, with both input and output ground terminals grounded to the computer chassis. In order to simplify the drawing of circuit diagrams, the ground terminals are not shown, and the internal amplifier is represented by a pie-shaped wedge with the apex pointing in the output direction. The idea here is that an amplifier is a unidirectional device; a signal fed to the input results in an output, but a signal placed across the output terminals will not result in a

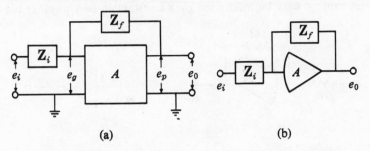

(a)   (b)

FIGURE 4.1.   (a) *Actual connections for operational amplifier;*
(b) *simplified symbol for* (a).

41

signal at the input terminals. The actual connections for an operational amplifier are shown in Figure 4.1(a), with the internal amplifier represented by a rectangle. The simplified symbol for the circuit of Figure 4.1(a) is given in Figure 4.1(b).

Note that here the pie-shaped wedge represents the internal amplifier only. In the following sections, the gain expressions for various computing networks will be derived. In these sections, the appropriate symbol for each network will be shown. These symbols are not used universally, but they were chosen because of their simplicity and the fact that they are easy to draw.

★ Change of Sign

The polarity of an input voltage can be reversed by using identical resistors in the input and feedback positions, as in Figure 4.2(a). The symbol for the entire network is the triangle shown in Figure 4.2(b), with the numeral 1 included to indicate that the closed-loop gain is one.

From Equation (51), if both Z_f and Z_i are one megohm resistors, for instance, then

$$G = \frac{e_0}{e_i} = -\frac{R_f}{R_i} = -\frac{1,000,000}{1,000,000} = -1.$$

Then $e_0 = -e_i$, and the sign of the voltage has been reversed.

★ Multiplication by a Constant

A voltage may be multiplied by a constant in two ways. If the

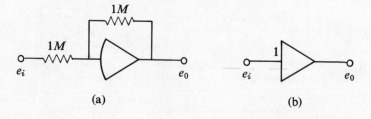

(a)   (b)

FIGURE 4.2.   (a) Operational amplifier circuit for changing sign;
(b) symbol for (a).

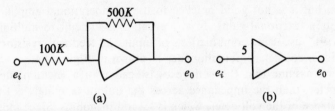

FIGURE 4.3. (a) Operation amplifier circuit for multiplying by −5.0; (b) symbol for (a).

constant is greater than 1.0, the operational amplifier is used to perform the multiplication. For instance, suppose it is desired to multiply a voltage by 5.0. If a feedback resistor having a resistance of 500,000 ohms is used with an input resistor of resistance 100,000 ohms, then

$$\mathbf{G} = \frac{e_0}{e_i} = -\frac{(500,000)}{(100,000)} = -5.0.$$

Then $e_0 = -5.0e_i$ (see Figure 4.3). Note that the polarity of the output voltage is opposite to that of the input voltage. This occurs whenever an operational amplifier is used.

If it is desired to multiply a voltage by a constant smaller than 1.0, a coefficient potentiometer is generally used. Obviously, if one wished to multiply by 0.200, the positions of the input and feedback resistors in Figure 4.3 can be reversed to give this desired

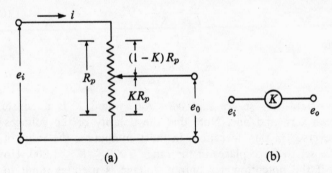

FIGURE 4.4. (a) Ideal coefficient potentiometer as a constant multiplier; (b) symbol for coefficient potentiometer.

result, but it is not good practice to use an operational amplifier to obtain fractional gains. In any event, it is difficult to multiply by 0.191, say, using combinations of input and feedback resistors. The ideal coefficient potentiometer is shown in Figure 4.4.

If we assume that the voltage e_0 is read with a vacuum tube voltmeter, then the impedance across the output terminals is the impedance of the voltmeter, which is several megohms. Since most coefficient potentiometers have resistances R_p in the range 10,000 to 100,000 ohms, essentially all current flows through the potentiometer, and negligible current flows in the output leads. The potentiometer current is

$$i = \frac{e_i}{R_p}. \tag{57}$$

The output voltage is the voltage drop across resistance KR_p,

$$e_0 = iKR_p, \tag{58}$$

which rearranges to

$$i = \frac{e_0}{KR_p}. \tag{59}$$

If no current flows in the output leads, then the current of Equation (57) is the same current given in Equation (59). Upon equating the two expressions,

$$\frac{e_i}{R_p} = \frac{e_0}{KR_p}. \tag{60}$$

Then,

$$\frac{e_0}{e_i} = \frac{KR_p}{R_p} = K. \tag{61}$$

Equation (61) shows that $e_0 = Ke_i$, where K is a constant between zero and one. Note that the polarity of the voltages is *not* reversed in this operation. In most computers, the value of K can be set to three places in the range $0.000 \le K \le 1.000$. However, if the potentiometer output voltage is used as input to a following operational amplifier or other electrical circuit, then there is a *loading* effect. This loading effect results from the fact

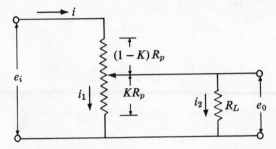

FIGURE 4.5.   *Coefficient potentiometer with resistance load.*

that current *does* flow in the output leads, thus causing the ratio of e_0 to e_i to be different from the value of K set on the potentiometer. The following discussion of potentiometer loading will show how this practice can give rise to errors.

Figure 4.5 shows a potentiometer with an output load resistance. The effective resistance "seen" by the current i consists of the parallel combination of R_L and KR_p in series with $(1 - K)R_p$. This effective resistance is

$$R_E = \frac{(KR_p)(R_L)}{KR_p + R_L} + (1 - K)R_p$$

$$= \frac{KR_pR_L + (1 - K)R_p(KR_p + R_L)}{KR_p + R_L} \tag{62}$$

$$= \frac{R_p(KR_L + KR_p + R_L - K^2R_p - KR_L)}{KR_p + R_L}$$

$$= \frac{R_p(KR_p + R_L - K^2R_p)}{KR_p + R_L}.$$

The input voltage equals the current times the effective resistance, or

$$e_i = iR_E \tag{63}$$

$$i = \frac{e_i(KR_p + R_L)}{R_p(KR_p + R_L - K^2R_p)}. \tag{64}$$

Also, the branch currents i_1 and i_2 are

$$i_1 = \frac{e_0}{KR_p} \tag{65}$$

$$i_2 = \frac{e_0}{R_L}. \tag{66}$$

By summing currents at the potentiometer contact,

$$i = i_1 + i_2. \tag{67}$$

By substituting Equations (64), (65), and (66) into Equation (67), one can obtain

$$\frac{e_0}{e_i} = \frac{KR_L}{KR_p + R_L - K^2R_p}. \tag{68}$$

Comparison of Equation (68) with Equation (61) allows the effect of loading of the potentiometer to be evaluated. Suppose that $K = 0.500$, and that both R_p and R_L are 100,000 ohm resistors. Then Equation (61) predicts that $\frac{e_0}{e_i} = 0.500$, but Equation (68) gives:

$$\frac{e_0}{e_i} = \frac{(0.500)(100,000)}{(0.500)(100,000) + 100,000 - (0.250)(100,000)} = \frac{50,000}{125,000}.$$

$$\frac{e_0}{e_i} = 0.400.$$

Equation (68) shows that the actual multiplication factor is 0.400, rather than the 0.500 setting which was used, an error of 20 per cent. This error can be avoided by setting the potentiometer with the load applied, and adjusting it until the desired output voltage is obtained. Or, if R_L is known, the proper value of K can be computed from Equation (68), and this value is then used for the potentiometer setting.

At the beginning of this section, an example was given in which a voltage was multiplied by 5.0. This is possible with some computers, if the necessary resistors are available. However, it is not so easy to multiply by 4.37, say, if only input and feedback re-

sistor are used. Here, of course, one can multiply the input
signal by 0.874 using a coefficient potentiometer, and then multiply
the reduced signal by 5.0 with the circuit of Figure 4.3, thus
giving an output voltage of $e_0 = -(0.874)(5)e_i = -4.37e_i$.

★ **Addition**

In order to add two quantities on an analog computer, the
voltages which represent the two quantities are fed in as parallel
inputs. The circuit for performing this operation is shown in
Figure 4.6.

For the internal amplifier, the open-loop gain is $A = e_0/e_g$,
where e_g is the voltage at the input grid of the amplifier. Then the
grid voltage is e_0/A, as indicated in Figure 4.6. A summation of
currents at the grid yields

$$i_1 + i_2 = i_3. \tag{69}$$

For current i_1,

$$e_1 - \frac{e_0}{A} = i_1 R_1, \tag{70}$$

$$i_1 = \frac{e_1 - \dfrac{e_0}{A}}{R_1}. \tag{71}$$

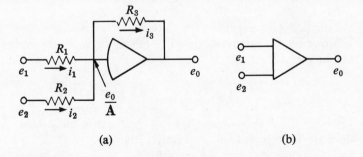

(a)   (b)

FIGURE 4.6.   (a) *Addition circuit for adding two quantities;*
(b) *symbol for above.*

Similarly,

$$i_2 = \frac{e_2 - \dfrac{e_0}{A}}{R_2}, \tag{72}$$

$$i_3 = \frac{\dfrac{e_0}{A} - e_0}{R_3}. \tag{73}$$

Note that instantaneous values are being used here for current and voltage, and therefore the input voltage waveform need not be sinusoidal or even periodic. The equations are entirely general for any kind of input voltage waveform. By substituting Equations (71), (72), and (73) into Equation (69) we obtain,

$$\frac{e_1 - \dfrac{e_0}{A}}{R_1} + \frac{e_2 - \dfrac{e_0}{A}}{R_2} = \frac{\dfrac{e_0}{A} - e_0}{R_3}. \tag{74}$$

Now, if A is very large, then e_0/A is negligible, and Equation (74) becomes

$$\frac{e_1}{R_1} + \frac{e_2}{R_2} = \frac{-e_0}{R_3}. \tag{75}$$

Upon rearranging Equation (75),

$$e_0 = -\left(\frac{R_3}{R_1} e_1 + \frac{R_3}{R_2} e_2 \right). \tag{76}$$

Equation (76) expresses the output voltage resulting from the addition of two input voltages. If n inputs are used, the equation can be generalized to

$$e_0 = -\left(\frac{R_3}{R_1} e_1 + \frac{R_3}{R_2} e_2 + \cdots + \frac{R_3}{R_n} e_n \right). \tag{77}$$

Obviously, if $R_1 = R_2 = R_3 = \cdots = R_n$, then the voltages add directly. If it is desired to multiply the individual voltages by various constants, then the ratio R_3/R_n may be set equal to this constant, if the constant is an integer. If the constant is not an integer, but is greater than 1.0, a coefficient potentiometer is used

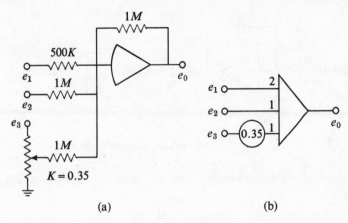

FIGURE 4.7. (a) *Circuit for performing* $e_0 = -(2e_1 + e_2 + 0.35 e_3)$.
(b) *symbol for above.*

ahead of R_n. If the constant is less than 1.0, the branch resistor is made equal to R_3, and the value of the constant is set on a coefficient potentiometer ahead of the branch resistor.

To illustrate, consider the operation $e_0 = -(2e_1 + e_2 + 0.35e_3)$. The circuit and the symbol for this addition are shown in Figure 4.7.

★ Subtraction

The circuit used for subtraction is identical to that shown in Figure 4.6 for addition. In operation, the voltage or voltages to be subtracted are fed into the circuit with negative polarities.

★ Integration

The circuit for performing integration uses an input resistor and a feedback capacitor, as shown in Figure 4.8. As in previous developments, current i_1 flows in the input resistor, current i_2 flows in the feedback element, and the grid current is considered negligible. Then,

$$i_1 = i_2. \tag{78}$$

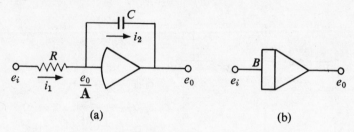

FIGURE 4.8.   (a) *Integration circuit; (b) symbol for above.*

By exactly the same reasoning used in obtaining Equations (70) and (71),

$$i_1 = \frac{e_1 - \dfrac{e_0}{\mathbf{A}}}{R}.$$ (79)

To obtain an expression for i_2, use must be made of the fact that the voltage drop across a capacitor is equal to $\dfrac{1}{C}\displaystyle\int_0^t i\, dt$, where C is the capacitance in farads and t is time. Then,

$$\frac{e_0}{\mathbf{A}} - e_0 = \frac{1}{C}\int_0^t i_2 dt.$$ (80)

By differentiating both sides and multiplying through by C,

$$C\frac{d}{dt}\left(\frac{e_0}{\mathbf{A}} - e_0\right) = i_2.$$ (81)

Substitution of Equations (79) and (81) into Equation (78) yields

$$\frac{e_i - \dfrac{e_0}{\mathbf{A}}}{R} = C\frac{d}{dt}\left(\frac{e_0}{\mathbf{A}} - e_0\right).$$ (82)

If $\mathbf{A}$ is large, $e_0/\mathbf{A}$ is negligibly small, and may be dropped. Then Equation (82) becomes

$$\frac{e_i}{R} = C\frac{d}{dt}(-e_0).$$ (83)

By rearranging,

$$-\frac{de_0}{dt} = \frac{e_i}{RC}.$$ (84)

By integrating between limits we get

$$e_0 = -\frac{1}{RC}\int_0^t e_i dt + E_0,$$ (85)

where E_0 is the value of e_0 at $t = 0$. Equation (85) shows that the output voltage of the circuit of Figure 4.8 is $1/RC$ times the integral of the input voltage with respect to time, plus the initial value of e_0. As in all other cases where an operational amplifier is used, the polarity of the output voltage is opposite to that of the input voltage.

Dimensionally, R is rated in ohms and C in farads. Since a farad is an ampere-second per volt, the product RC has dimensions of (ohms) (amperes) (seconds)/(volt), or seconds. This product is called a *time constant*, about which more will be said in Chapter 5. If R is one megohm (1×10^6 ohms), and C is one microfarad (1×10^{-6} farad), then $RC = 1$ second, and $1/RC$ is 1 sec^{-1}. The value of $1/RC$ is the constant B in Figure 4.8(b). This value can be changed by appropriate choice of the values of R and C.

The summing integrator can perform both addition (or subtraction) and integration. The output voltage is expressed by

$$e_0 = -\frac{1}{C}\int_0^t \left(\frac{e_1}{R_1} + \frac{e_2}{R_2} + \cdots + \frac{e_n}{R_n}\right)dt + E_0.$$ (86)

The proof of Equation (86) is left to the reader. The circuit and the symbol for performing the operation $e_0 = -\int_0^t (e_1 + 10e_2)dt$ are shown in Figure 4.9, with $E_0 = 0$.

The application of initial conditions to integrating amplifiers merits some discussion. An integrating circuit will integrate whatever grid signal is applied, and even though no signal is being fed into the input grid of an integrating amplifier, there will still be a small signal on the grid, both ac and dc, resulting from static charges, stray pickup, and so on. The output of the in-

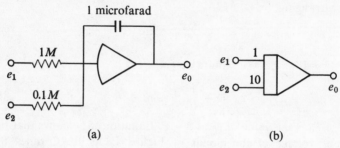

FIGURE 4.9.   (a) *Circuit for performing* $e_0 = -\int_0^t (e_1 + 10\,e_2)\,dt;$
(b) *symbol for above.*

tegrator will be a function of the size of the "noise" signal and
the length of time the signal has been applied. Thus, the output
voltages of the various integrators in a circuit might have any
arbitrary value at a particular time, instead of the value of E_0
required by the problem at hand.

In order to avoid this situation, relays are used with all integrating amplifiers. A relay is connected from the output of the
amplifier back to the input, thus short-circuiting the capacitor
and preventing it from accumulating any charge. When the
problem is ready to be run, the operating switch is closed, the
relays open, and the integrator begins to function. Since all
relays open at the same time, this arrangement causes all the
integrating amplifiers to begin operation at the same time. In

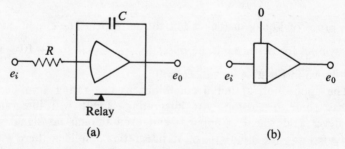

FIGURE 4.10.   (a) *Integrating amplifier with zero initial condition;*
(b) *symbol for above*

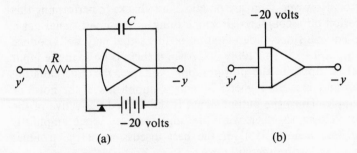

FIGURE 4.11.   (a) *Integrating amplifier with intial condition of $y(0) = 20$ volts; (b) symbol for above.*

Heathkit computers, the relays must be connected to the integrating amplifiers with patch cords, whereas in other computers (Donner; Electronic Associates, Inc.; Applied Dynamics, Inc.) these relays are internally connected to the integrating amplifiers and require no connections by the operator. Figure 4.10 shows an integrating amplifier with zero initial conditions.

When nonzero initial conditions are to be used, the connections shown in Figure 4.10 must be modified. Since the computer variables are voltages, the initial conditions for the equation to be solved must be entered as voltages. The initial condition is the E_0 of Equation (85) and is applied by charging the capacitor of the integrating amplifier so that the voltage drop across the capacitor is equal to E_0 volts at time $t = 0$. This is done by inserting an initial condition power supply of the proper voltage and polarity in series with the relay. The capacitor charges up to the polarity of the initial condition power supply, and when the relay opens, the power supply is disconnected from the amplifier. Figure 4.11 shows the circuit and the symbol for an integrating amplifier with the initial condition $y(0) = 20$ volts. Since the output of the amplifier is $-y$, the initial condition voltage is -20 volts.

★ **Differentiation of a Variable**

It is theoretically possible to differentiate with an operational amplifier, using a capacitor in the input position and a feedback *differentiation*

resistor. However, there are practical drawbacks to performing this operation on a computer. For one thing, if the input signal has a steep enough slope, differentiation of this signal may well produce an output in excess of 100 volts. Also, if there is noise in the input signal or ripple in the power supply voltages, the differentiating circuit amplifies the higher frequency components of the noise or the ripple. Thus, the output signal is the desired derivative of the input voltage together with the superimposed (and amplified) noise. See Jackson [18] for the best discussion of the troubles encountered with differentiators.

As a result of these difficulties, differentiation is an operation which is rarely performed on an analog computer. It can nearly always be avoided by rewriting the set of equations which is to be solved. If differentiation *cannot* be avoided, there are some approximate differentiation circuits which reduce the amount of noise produced [18].

★ Multiplication of a Variable by a Variable

The operations which have been discussed thus far allow the solution only of linear differential equations with constant coefficients. Since such equations can be solved analytically by various well-known methods, it would many times be questionable whether the use of an analog computer would be justified, if this were the limit of the machine's capabilities.

There are many systems in which nonlinear behavior is encountered. Analytical solution of such systems is often messy, and in any event requires a degree of mathematical sophistication which many scientists and engineers do not possess. Thus many researchers, when faced with a problem involving nonlinearities, will study the nonlinearity in the region of expected operation and approximate the behavior by a straight line (thus obtaining a *linear* differential equation describing the system in the operating region).

The use of function multipliers with analog computers allows the machine solution of nonlinear equations and equations with variable coefficients, thus extending the usefulness of analog computing equipment enormously. There is a variety of equipment available for function multiplication. Essentially, such equipment operates on two variable input signals, x and y, to produce an output Kxy, where K is a proportionality constant.

The two main types of multipliers are the electromechanical and the electronic devices. The servomultiplier is an example of the first type, and is the most widely used of the various multipliers. The device contains a servo motor which rotates a shaft common to several matched potentiometers, which have certain voltages across their terminals. An input signal x fed to the servomultiplier is amplified and applied to the windings of the servo motor, causing it to rotate. Another input signal y is placed across the terminals of one of the potentiometers, and a reference voltage k is placed across the terminals of another potentiometer. Rotation of the motor causes rotation of the potentiometer contacts, and the voltage picked off the reference potentiometer is continuously compared to the input voltage, x. When the two voltages are equal, the motor ceases to rotate, and the output voltage is then $\frac{1}{k}xy = Kxy$. Then the two variables x and y have been multiplied. The interested reader is referred to Byrant, Just, and Pawlicki [19] and Johnson [20] for a more detailed discussion of the operation of servomultipliers.

Servomultipliers are low in cost, simple and reliable in operation, easy to adjust, and small in size. The chief disadvantage to their use is their frequency response, the usable frequencies being limited to a range varying from 0–5 cps to 0–50 cps.

The most commonly used of the electronic multipliers is the time division multiplier. These devices form the algebraic product of two variables by averaging several cycles of a rectangular-type waveform generated from the two input variables. The method by which the multiplication is achieved is complicated, and will not be discussed here, but see Wass [21]. Johnson [22] also has a readable and less technical discussion.

Electronic multipliers have high accuracy and they are usable to frequencies around 2000 cps. They are relatively expensive, and more complicated than servomultipliers, but their greater frequency range allows them to be used where the servomultipliers will not serve.

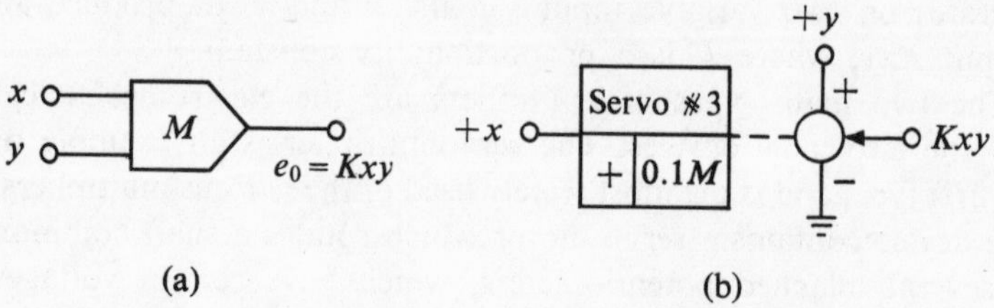

FIGURE 4.12.   (a) *General symbol for variable multiplier;*
(b) *symbol for servomultiplier.*

There are other specialized multipliers which produce outputs proportional to the square, square root, logarithm, or power of the input, and division is also possible. These will not be discussed here, but see Wass [23] or Johnson [24].

The general symbol for a variable multiplier is shown in Figure 4.12(a). A special symbol is often used for the servomultiplier, since it requires a loading resistor, and thus involves more than just input and output terminals. A common symbol for a servo-multiplier is shown in Figure 4.12(b). The information inside the box includes the number of the servomultiplier being used, the polarity of the reference potentiometer voltage ($+$ or $-$), and the value of the load resistor (LD) used with the multiplier.

★   Function Generation

The solution of problems on an analog computer often requires the use of some arbitrary function to serve as the forcing function. This function must be fed to the input of an operational amplifier, and therefore must be available as a voltage which varies with time in the same way that the desired dependent variable varies with the independent variable.

There are many ways in which such functions may be generated, the most common being the generation of the function directly on the computer or the use of a diode straight-line-segment function generator.

As an example of functions which can be generated directly on the computer, consider the equations

$$f(t) = 10 \sin \omega t \tag{87}$$

$$f'(t) = 10\omega \cos \omega t \tag{88}$$

$$f''(t) = -10\omega^2 \sin \omega t. \tag{89}$$

Comparison of Equation (87) with Equation (89) reveals that

$$f''(t) = -\omega^2 f(t). \tag{90}$$

Equation (90) can be solved on the computer, using the initial conditions $f(0) = 0$, $f'(0) = 10\omega$, which are the values of $f(t)$ and $f'(t)$ at $t = 0$. The result of the first integration is ω times the cosine function, and the result of the second integration is the sine function.

As another example, negative exponentials in t can be generated by solving the first-order differential equation

$$\frac{dy}{dt} + \alpha y = 0. \tag{91}$$

The solution of this equation is

$$y(t) = Be^{-\alpha t}. \tag{92}$$

Proper choice of computer settings and the value of the RC product for the integrating amplifier allow the variation of B and α to generate various exponential decay functions.

Diode function generators approximate a given function by a series of straight line segments. Consider the function shown in Figure 4.13. The straight line segments which the function generator produces have variable slopes and variable *break points*, a break point being the point of intersection of two of the straight line segments. The diodes in the function generator are biased so that no current will flow in a diode until the applied voltage reaches a certain value. Also, the output voltage of a diode is proportional to the input voltage, and the proportionality relationship (the slope of the plot of output voltage versus input voltage) can be varied by varying the resistance through which the output current

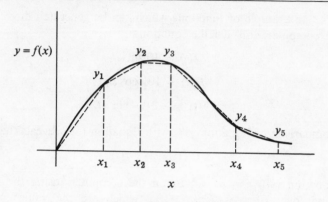

FIGURE 4.13.   *An arbitrary function of X.*

flows. Thus, the first line segment in Figure 4.13 is set up by using a break voltage of zero volts and a slope of y_1/x_1. The second straight line segment has a break voltage of x_1 volts and a slope of $\dfrac{y_2 - y_1}{x_2 - x_1}$, and so on. The more straight line segments which are available in the diode function generator, the more closely the approximation approaches the desired function.

Diode function generators are relatively low in cost, easy to use, and are accurate to 0.2 to 5 percent, depending upon the number of diodes available. The interested reader is referred to Jackson [25], Korn and Korn [26], and Johnson [27] for more detailed discussions and circuit diagrams of diode function generators. Jackson and Korn and Korn also discuss the use of diode function generators to obtain functions of two variables.

Other types of function generators include tapped potentiometers, curve followers, and cathode-ray types (the photoformer). These will not be discussed here, but are adequately treated in the above references.

V

Time Scaling

An equation or set of equations describing a physical process or system is a mathematical model of that process or system. In order to obtain an analog computer solution, an analog model of the equations is set up on the computer. The variables in the physical process must be related to the variables in the analog model (usually voltages) in order for the analog model to have meaning. The variables of the mathematical model are related to the variables of the analog model by magnitude scale factors and time scale factors.

The independent variable in the computer is time. The independent variable in the problem, whatever it may be, varies in the same way as computer time. The computer dependent variables are the output voltages of the operational amplifiers, and the dependent variables of the problem vary in a manner analogous to the variation of these output voltages.

Since the output voltage of most computing amplifiers is limited to an operating range of -100 volts to $+100$ volts, the equations to be solved must be examined, and perhaps altered, so that the maximum value of a dependent variable in the equation will not cause the corresponding computer dependent variable to exceed a value of 100 volts. The process of adjusting the equations to limit the magnitudes of the computer dependent variables is called *magnitude scaling*, and will be discussed in Chapter 6.

The computer operator may wish to speed a problem up or slow it down in order to get the maximum information from the solution. Also, some solutions are oscillatory in nature, and the recording device being used may be unable to provide a satisfactory trace of the solution at the frequency of the original equation. The latter situation requires that the solution be slowed down so that the frequency of oscillation of the solution is within the capabilities of the recorder. It is possible to adjust the equations to be solved over a wide range of solution times, and this adjustment process is known as *time scaling*.

★ Time Constant

The term *time constant* will come up shortly, and needs to be defined. Consider the following series resistance-inductance (*RL*) circuit. When the switch *S* is closed, current begins to flow in the

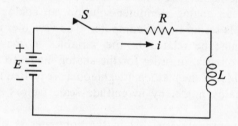

FIGURE 5.1. *Series RL circuit.*

circuit of Figure 5.1, and it builds up to the steady-state value. It is desired to derive an expression for this current as a function of time. By writing Kirchhoff's voltage equation around the circuit,

$$L\frac{di}{dt} + Ri = E. \tag{93}$$

The general solution of this equation is the sum of the complementary function (the solution of the reduced equation) and the particular integral. The reduced equation is

$$L\frac{di}{dt} + Ri = 0. \tag{94}$$

By using the integrating factor $e^{(R/L)t}$, we can write

$$d(ie^{(R/L)t}) = 0. \tag{95}$$

Then the complementary function is

$$i = Ke^{-(R/L)t}. \tag{96}$$

To obtain the particular integral, assume that i is of the form $i = A + Bt$, then di/dt is equal to B. By substituting these values into Equation (93), we obtain

$$LB + R(A + Bt) = E. \tag{97}$$

Upon equating like coefficients, it is found that $B = 0$, then $i = A = E/R$, which is the particular integral. Then the general solution of Equation (93) is

$$i = \frac{E}{R} + Ke^{-(R/L)t}. \tag{98}$$

When $t = 0$, $i = 0$, then $K = -(E/R)$. Thus, the equation relating current and time for the circuit of Figure 5.1 is

$$i = \frac{E}{R} - \frac{E}{R}e^{-(R/L)t} = \frac{E}{R}(1 - e^{-(R/L)t}). \tag{99}$$

Obviously, any values of R and L may be used in such a circuit. However, it would be nice to characterize the behavior of such circuits simply, and in making calculations, the simplest case is the one in which e occurs to the first power. If the ratio L/R is made equal to t, then the exponent of e is -1, or

$$i = \frac{E}{R}\Big(1 - \frac{1}{e}\Big) = \frac{E}{R}(1 - 0.37) = 0.63\frac{E}{R}. \tag{100}$$

In other words, when $t = L/R$, the current in an RL circuit is 0.63 of the final value. The solution to Equation (100) is shown in Figure 5.2.

There are many systems which give a response such as the one shown in Figure 5.2. By common agreement, one time constant has been defined to be the time required for a variable to change 63 per cent of the difference between the initial and final values. The time constant is equal to the time required to make the

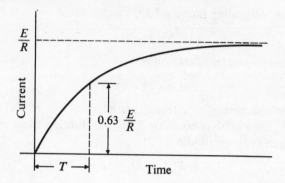

FIGURE 5.2. *Current as a function of time in a series RL circuit.*

exponent of *e* equal to -1, regardless of the physical system involved. The time constant is expressed in units of time, and in this text it will be represented by *T*.

★ Frequency Responses of Commonly-Used Recording Devices

One of the inherent advantages of an analog computer is that the time of solution can be varied over a considerable range, that is, a problem can be run much faster, or much slower, than the physical process. However, there are several things which must be considered in selecting the time scale factor for a particular problem. One of these factors is the frequency of oscillation of the equation.

It is often desirable to obtain a recording of the results of an analog computation. Thus, the equation frequencies must be adjusted to the range of frequencies which can be handled by the recorder being used. If the frequency of the computer output voltage exceeds the recommended frequency response of the particular recording device in use, then transients generated in the recorder itself will affect the recording. As frequencies continue to increase, some recorders will experience increasing difficulty in following the results, and the amplitudes will become progressively smaller than they should be. In the extreme case, the frequency may be so high that the computing amplifiers are operating in the region where the gain and phase characteristic curves are no longer flat, in which case the results are highly questionable. This last could only occur when an oscilloscope or oscillograph is used as the readout device, because any other type of recorder will have deposited its ink on the walls and ceiling before frequencies of this magnitude are reached.

The following ranges of frequencies are suggested for various kinds of recording devices.

1. With *any* recording device, a frequency of less than one cycle in about five minutes should be avoided, since accumulation of errors and drift in the computing amplifiers are magnified in long computing runs.

2. Servo-driven recorders, such as X-Y plotters, cannot handle frequencies higher than about two cycles per second (around 12 radians per second). In addition, the plotting speed in inches per second must be considered if curves of large amplitude are to be recorded. These devices are generally quite accurate.

3. Galvanometer-type recorders, which draw the curve on a moving strip of paper, have maximum frequencies of 60 to 200 cps. If the amplitude of the trace is only half of the allowable full-scale deflection, these recorders have an accuracy of about ± 0.5 percent of full scale. However, if full-scale deflection is allowed, the accuracy falls to about ± 5 percent of full scale.

4. Cathode-ray oscilloscopes are used chiefly for visual monitoring of the computer output. The scope used should have both dc and ac amplifiers, since ac scopes are not normally dependable at frequencies below about 40 cps. With both ac and dc amplifiers, the scope has a frequency range extending from zero cps to several hundred kilocycles, which is beyond the frequency range of most computer components. Permanent records of the scope traces may be made by photographing them, but this method is rather expensive.

★ Determination of the Frequency of an Equation

The frequency of oscillation of the solutions of a differential equation must be known before an intelligent choice of time-scale factor can be made. This frequency can be approximated by finding the undamped natural frequencies of second-order or higher-order differential equations, while the reciprocal of the time constant is used as a rough estimate of frequency for first-order equations. Consider the following equation:

$$A_1\frac{dx}{dt} + A_2x = A_3y. \tag{101}$$

The solution of the reduced equation gives the transient portion of the complete solution of the equation. The reduced equation is

$$A_1\frac{dx}{dt} + A_2x = 0. \tag{102}$$

The solution of Equation (102) is

$$x = Ke^{-(A_2/A_1)t} = Ke^{-(t/T)}, \tag{103}$$

where T is the time constant, and is equal to

$$T = \frac{A_1}{A_2}. \tag{104}$$

Then the approximate frequency of the equation is the reciprocal of the time constant, or,

$$\omega = \frac{1}{T} = \frac{A_2}{A_1}. \tag{105}$$

As proof of this last statement, consider Figure 5.3. Curve A is the plot of the solution to Equation (103), an exponential decay curve. In a period of time equal to one time constant, Curve A has passed through 63 percent of its total change, and its value at time T is $K(1 - 0.63) = 0.37K$.

Curve B is part of a sine wave which has an amplitude equal to K and an angular velocity equal to ω radians per second. It has been constructed to intersect Curve A at the point $t = T$. At this point, $\sin(T + 180°) = 0.37K$. The sine wave oscillates about the ordinate $x = K$, and with respect to this ordinate, the value of $\sin(T + 180°) = -0.63K$. Since the angle is greater than 180° for the portion shown, the negative value is consistent. The angle $(T + 180°)$ is approximately 220°, so T is about 40°, or $(40/180)\pi = 2\pi/9$ radians. If we assume that $T = 2$ seconds, then the angular

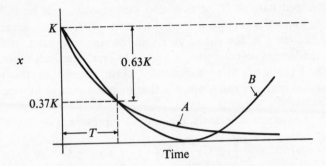

FIGURE 5.3. *Plot of the solution of equation* (103)
(curve A) with superimposed sine wave (curve B).

velocity of the sine wave is $2\pi/9$ divided by 2, or 0.35 radian per second. For the exponential decay curve, if T is equal to the assumed 2 seconds, then $1/T$ is 0.50, which is close to the 0.35 obtained for the sine wave.

The aim is to find out how fast the various computer components and the recorder will have to respond in order to follow the solution. Figure 5.3 shows that Curve A has very nearly the same rate of change as the sine wave until the point $t = T$ is reached. Beyond that point, the rate of change of Curve A is less than that of the sine wave. Then if the computer and its associated recorder can follow the sine wave, they can follow the exponential curve, and $1/T$ gives an approximation to the angular velocity of the sine wave which intersects the exponential curve at $t = T$ and has the same amplitude as the exponential curve.

A second-order differential equation has the form

$$B_1\frac{d^2x}{dt^2} + B_2\frac{dx}{dt} + B_3x = B_4y. \tag{106}$$

The undamped natural frequency of this equation is, by definition

$$\omega_{n,x} = \sqrt{\frac{B_3}{B_1}}. \tag{107}$$

Actually, ω_n is not the frequency, but the angular velocity. However, current usage is such that practically everyone refers to ω_n as the undamped natural frequency, and that practice will be followed here. The value obtained from Equation (107) is not necessarily the frequency of the equation, since damping may exist, and ω_n is the *undamped* natural frequency. However, the value obtained from Equation (107) is normally close enough to the actual equation frequency to show whether or not a change in time scale is indicated.

A third-order differential equation is represented by

$$C_1 \frac{d^3y}{dt^3} + C_2 \frac{d^2y}{dt^2} + C_3 \frac{dy}{dt} + C_4 y = C_5 x. \tag{108}$$

The undamped natural frequency for Equation (108) may be obtained by application of the Routh criterion for stability. The method of obtaining the Routh array is given by Johnson [28], but the result is the same as that for the second-order equation. That is, the undamped natural frequency is equal to the square root of the zero-order term divided by the second-order term, or

$$\omega_{n,y} = \sqrt{\frac{C_4}{C_2}} \tag{109}$$

for Equation (108).

There is no handy mathematical approximation for determining the undamped natural frequency of differential equations of higher than third order. Johnson [29] recommends that the coefficients of the terms be examined. If the higher-order coefficients have values close to those of the lower-order coefficients, the equation will have a frequency of the order of one radian per second. If the values of the coefficients of the higher-order terms are markedly different from the coefficients of the lower-order terms, a change in time scale is indicated. Experimentation with several time-scale factors will indicate a factor which will bring the higher-order coefficients close to the lower-order coefficients.

ILLUSTRATIVE EXAMPLES

The following equations are to be solved with an analog computer. What are the equation frequencies, and what kinds of

recording equipment could be used to trace out the solutions?
(1)

$$\frac{d^2c}{dt^2} + 10\frac{dc}{dt} + 25c = 10 \sin 10t.$$

This is a second-order equation, and the undamped natural frequency is $(25/1)^{0.5}$ = 5.0 radians per second. This is a frequency of $5.0/2\pi$, or about 0.8 cycle per second. An X-Y plotter can be used here if the amplitude of the curves is not made so large that the allowable plotting speed is exceeded. Without question, a galvanometer-type recorder or a dc oscilloscope could be used.
(2)

$$3\frac{dx}{dt} + 50x = 40.$$

The time constant of this equation is 3/50, then the approximate angular velocity of the solution is 50/3 = 16.7 radians per second. This is a frequency of about 2.7 cycles per second. A galvanometer-type recorder or a dc oscilloscope could be used, but this frequency is too high for an X-Y plotter, and the equation should be slowed down by a factor of two or more if an X-Y plotter is to be used.
(3)

$$10\frac{d^3y}{dt^3} + 3\frac{d^2y}{dt^2} + 5\frac{dy}{dt} + 13y = f(t).$$

This equation is third-order, and the undamped natural frequency is the square root of the zero-order term divided by the second-order term, or $(13/3)^{0.5}$ = 2.1 radians per second. The recorder used may be an X-Y plotter, a galvanometer-type recorder, or a dc oscilloscope.

★ **Performance of the Time-Scale Change**

When it has been decided that a change in time scale is desirable, a change in variable is made for time, the independent variable in the equation. Thus, the substitution is made

$$t = \frac{\tau}{a}, \tag{110}$$

where a is the time-scale factor, t is the real time variable, and τ is the computer time variable. Thus, if the problem solution is to be slowed down ten times, then $a = 10$. Similarly, if it is desired to speed the solution up by a factor of ten, then $a = 0.1$.

ILLUSTRATIVE EXAMPLE

Suppose that the following equation is to be solved:

$$\frac{d^2i}{dt^2} + 40\frac{di}{dt} + 100i = 100 \cos t,$$

with the initial conditions $i(0) = d^2i(0)/dt^2 = 0$, $di(0)/dt = 2.5$. The undamped natural frequency of this equation is equal to the square root of 100, or 10 radians per second. Suppose that it is desired to slow the solution down by a factor of five. Then $t = \tau/5$, and

$$\frac{di}{dt} = \frac{di}{d\left(\dfrac{\tau}{5}\right)} = 5\frac{di}{d\tau}$$

$$\frac{d^2i}{dt^2} = \frac{d}{dt}\left[5\frac{di}{d\tau}\right] = \frac{d}{d\left(\dfrac{\tau}{5}\right)}\left[5\frac{di}{d\tau}\right]$$

$$= 25\frac{d^2i}{d\tau^2}.$$

By making the above substitutions in the equation which was to be solved,

$$25\frac{d^2i}{d\tau^2} + 200\frac{di}{d\tau} + 100i = 100 \cos 0.2\tau.$$

The undamped natural frequency of this equation is the square root of 100/25, which is two radians per second (of computer time). Thus, the problem has been slowed down by a factor of five as desired. However, there is an initial condition which is time dependent, and it must also be scaled. Thus, if $di(0)/dt = 2.5$, then $5 di(0)/d\tau = 2.5$, and $di(0)/d\tau = 0.50$. Now the time-scale change for the problem is complete.

★ **The Standard Form of a Second-Order Differential Equation with Constant Coefficients**

At the risk of repeating material which may be familiar to the reader, the standard form of a second-order differential equation with constant coefficients will be reviewed so that the possible solutions to this type of equation are clearly understood. Also, the meaning and the effect of *damping* will be emphasized.

Consider an equation of the form

$$A\frac{d^2y}{dt^2} + B\frac{dy}{dt} + Cy = f(t). \tag{111}$$

The corresponding reduced equation is

$$A\frac{d^2y}{dt^2} + B\frac{dy}{dt} + Cy = 0. \tag{112}$$

A solution to Equation (112) is $y(t) = Ke^{mt}$, where K and m are constants. Then,

$$\frac{dy}{dt} = mKe^{mt}$$

$$\frac{d^2y}{dt^2} = m^2Ke^{mt}.$$

By making these substitutions in Equation (112) we obtain

$$Am^2Ke^{mt} + BmKe^{mt} + CKe^{mt} = 0$$

$$(Am^2 + Bm + C)Ke^{mt} = 0. \tag{113}$$

Since Ke^{mt} is never zero for finite values of t, even if m is a negative number, then it follows that

$$Am^2 + Bm + C = 0. \tag{114}$$

This equation is called the *characteristic equation*, and it has the two roots

$$m_1, m_2 = -\frac{B}{2A} \pm \frac{1}{2A}\sqrt{B^2 - 4AC}. \tag{115}$$

Then the solution of the reduced equation (Equation 112), which is the transient portion of the general solution of Equation (111), is

$$y(t) = K_1 e^{m_1 t} + K_2 e^{m_2 t}. \tag{116}$$

Now let us *define* the following two quantities:

$$\text{Undamped natural frequency} \atop \text{(radians per second)} = \omega_n = \sqrt{\frac{C}{A}}. \tag{117}$$

$$\text{Damping ratio (dimensionless)} = \zeta = \sqrt{\frac{B^2}{4AC}}. \tag{118}$$

Then
$$B = 2\zeta\sqrt{AC}. \tag{119}$$

Now, rearranging Equation (112),

$$\frac{d^2 y}{dt^2} + \frac{B}{A}\frac{dy}{dt} + \frac{C}{A}y = 0. \tag{120}$$

Upon substituting Equations (117) and (119) into Equation (120),

$$\frac{d^2 y}{dt^2} + \frac{2\zeta\sqrt{AC}}{A}\frac{dy}{dt} + \omega_n^2 y = 0$$

$$\frac{d^2 y}{dt^2} + 2\zeta\omega_n\frac{dy}{dt} + \omega_n^2 y = 0. \tag{121}$$

Equation (121) is called the *standard form* for a second-order differential equation with constant coefficients. The standard form has the characteristic equation

$$m^2 + 2\zeta\omega_n m + \omega_n^2 = 0. \tag{122}$$

The roots of this equation are:

$$m_1, m_2 = -\zeta\omega_n \pm \frac{1}{2}\sqrt{4\zeta^2\omega_n^2 - 4\omega_n^2}$$

$$= -\zeta\omega_n \pm \omega_n\sqrt{\zeta^2 - 1}. \tag{123}$$

Now let us examine the possible solutions of Equation (122). *Case 1:* $\zeta = 0$.

This case is tantamount to setting the coefficient of the first-order derivative equal to zero. The situation is referred to as *zero-damping*. The equation to be solved, in standard form, is then

$$\frac{d^2y}{dt^2} + \omega_n^2 y = 0, \tag{124}$$

and, since $\zeta = 0$, the roots of the characteristic equation are [see Equation (123)]

$$m_1, m_2 = -0 \pm \omega_n\sqrt{-1} = \pm j\omega_n.$$

Then the solution to Equation (124) is

$$y(t) = K_1 e^{+j\omega_n t} + K_2 e^{-j\omega_n t}. \tag{125}$$

Euler's equation provides the following relationships:

$$K_1 e^{+j\omega_n t} = K_1(\cos \omega_n t + j \sin \omega_n t) \tag{126}$$

$$K_2 e^{-j\omega_n t} = K_2(\cos \omega_n t - j \sin \omega_n t). \tag{127}$$

The solution of Equation (125) thus becomes

$$y(t) = K_3 \cos \omega_n t + K_4 \sin \omega_n t, \tag{128}$$

where $K_3 = K_1 + K_2$, and $K_4 = j(K_1 - K_2)$. If these constants are further defined as

$$K_3 = K \sin \Phi$$

$$K_4 = K \cos \Phi,$$

then Equation (128) can be written

$$y(t) = K \sin \Phi \cos \omega_n t + K \cos \Phi \sin \omega_n t$$
$$= K(\sin \Phi \cos \omega_n t + \cos \Phi \sin \omega_n t). \tag{129}$$

Now recalling the trigonometric identity

$$\sin (\omega_n t + \Phi) = \sin \omega_n t \cos \Phi + \cos \omega_n t \sin \Phi,$$

Equation (129) can be expressed in the form

$$y(t) = K \sin (\omega_n t + \Phi). \tag{130}$$

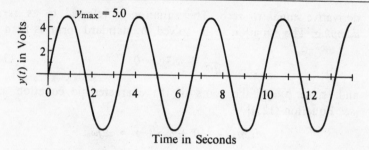

FIGURE 5.4.   *Solution of $y'' + 4y = 0$, illustrating the undamped case.*

The transient solution for the undamped case is thus seen to be a sinusoidal variation of amplitude K which has frequency equal to the undamped natural frequency of the equation. It will be noted that *the amplitude of the solution does not diminish with time*, so that the solution will oscillate forever.

In order to illustrate the form of the solution clearly, the equation $y'' + 4y = 0$ was solved on an analog computer with $y'(0) = 10$, $y(0) = 0$. The solution is shown in Figure 5.4.

Case 2: $0 < \zeta < 1$.

This situation represents the underdamped case. The roots of the characteristic equation are

$$m_1, m_2 = -\zeta\omega_n \pm \omega_n\sqrt{\zeta^2 - 1},$$

and since ζ is less than 1, $\zeta^2 - 1$ is a negative quantity. Then the roots are complex conjugates,

$$m_1, m_2 = -\zeta\omega_n \pm j\omega_n\sqrt{1 - \zeta^2}. \tag{131}$$

The transient part of the general solution is

$$y(t) = K_1 e^{-(\zeta\omega_n - j\omega_n\sqrt{1-\zeta^2})t} + K_2 e^{-(\zeta\omega_n + j\omega_n\sqrt{1-\zeta^2})t}$$

$$= K_1 e^{-\zeta\omega_n t} e^{+j\omega_n\sqrt{1-\zeta^2}t} + K_2 e^{-\zeta\omega_n t} e^{-j\omega_n\sqrt{1-\zeta^2}t}$$

$$= K_1 e^{-\zeta\omega_n t}(\cos \omega_n\sqrt{1 - \zeta^2}t + j \sin \omega_n\sqrt{1 - \zeta^2}t)$$

$$\quad + K_2 e^{-\zeta\omega_n t}(\cos \omega_n\sqrt{1 - \zeta^2}t - j \sin \omega_n\sqrt{1 - \zeta^2}t)$$

$$y(t) = e^{-\zeta\omega_n t}(K_3 \cos \omega_n\sqrt{1 - \zeta^2}t + K_4 \sin \omega_n\sqrt{1 - \zeta^2}t).$$

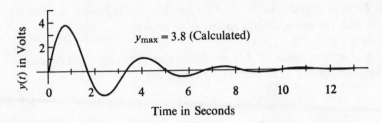

FIGURE 5.5. *The underdamped case, with $\zeta = 0.2$. Solution of the equation* $y'' + 0.8y' + 4y = 0$, *with* $y'(0) = 10$, $y(0) = 0$.

By defining $K_3 = K \sin \Phi$ and $K_4 = K \cos \Phi$, the last equation can be reduced to the form

$$y(t) = Ke^{-\zeta \omega_n t} \sin (\omega_n \sqrt{1 - \zeta^2} t + \Phi). \tag{132}$$

Equation (132) is a sinusoid having a frequency *smaller* than the undamped natural frequency of the differential equation, and the amplitude of $y(t)$ decreases with time. Thus the underdamped case, for which the roots of the characteristic equation are complex conjugates, gives a transient solution which is an exponentially-decaying sine wave.

To illustrate the underdamped case, the equation $y'' + 0.8y' + 4y = 0$ was solved, with initial conditions $y'(0) = 10$ and $y(0) = 0$. The damping ratio for this equation is 0.2. The computer solution is shown in Figure 5.5.

To illustrate further the underdamped case, consider a damping ratio of $\zeta = 0.6$. The differential equation becomes $y'' + 2.4y'$

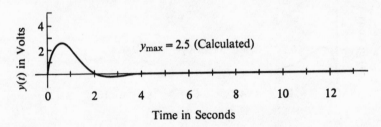

FIGURE 5.6. *The underdamped case with $\zeta = 0.6$. Solution of the equation* $y'' + 2.4y' + 4y = 0$, *with* $y'(0) = 10$, $y(0) = 0$.

$+ 4y = 0$. The computer solution for this case is shown in Figure 5.6, with the same initial conditions as above.

Case 3: $\zeta = 1.0$.

A damping ratio of 1.0 produces the critically damped case. The roots of the characteristic equation are

$$m_1, m_2 = -\zeta\omega_n \pm \omega_n\sqrt{\zeta^2 - 1} = -\omega_n. \tag{133}$$

The roots are thus real and repeated, and the transient solution is

$$y(t) = K_1 e^{-\omega_n t} + K_2 t e^{-\omega_n t}. \tag{134}$$

The solution is not a sinusoid, but decays exponentially with time. It has been shown that oscillatory solutions are obtained with damping ratios between zero and 1.0. With damping ratios equal to or greater than 1.0, oscillatory solutions are no longer encountered. Thus *critical* damping is the boundary between oscillatory and nonoscillatory behavior.

To illustrate critical damping, consider the differential equation

$$y'' + 4y' + 4y = 0,$$

with $y'(0) = 10$ and $y(0) = 0$. The damping ratio is seen to be 1.0. The computer solution of this equation is shown in Figure 5.7.

Case 4: $\zeta > 1.0$.

When the damping ratio has values greater than 1.0, the equation is overdamped. The roots of the characteristic equation are

$$m_1, m_2 = -\zeta\omega_n \pm \omega_n\sqrt{\zeta^2 - 1}. \tag{135}$$

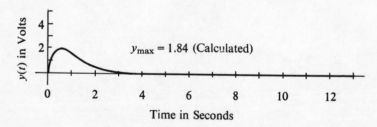

FIGURE 5.7. *The critically-damped case* ($\zeta = 1.0$). *Solution of the equation* $y'' + 4y' + 4y = 0$, *with* $y'(0) = 10$, $y(0) = 0$.

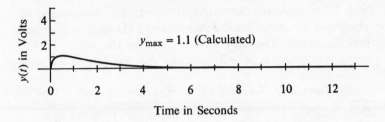

FIGURE 5.8. *The overdamped case, with $\zeta = 2$. Solution of the equation*
$y'' + 8y' + 4y = 0$, *with* $y' = 10$, $y(0) = 0$.

These roots are real and unequal. The transient solution is

$$y(t) = K_1 e^{(-\zeta\omega_n + \omega_n\sqrt{\zeta^2-1})t} + K_2 e^{(-\zeta\omega_n - \omega_n\sqrt{\zeta^2-1})t}$$

$$y(t) = e^{-\zeta\omega_n t}(K_1 e^{\omega_n\sqrt{\zeta^2-1}t} + K_2 e^{-\omega_n\sqrt{\zeta^2-1}t}). \tag{136}$$

The variable y will decay to zero with time. The larger the value of ζ used, the more rapidly the maximum value will be reached, but the longer the time required for the variable to return to zero.

To illustrate the overdamped case, consider the differential equation $y'' + 8y' + 4y = 0$, with $y'(0) = 10$, $y(0) = 0$. The damping coefficient is 2.0. The computer solution for this equation is given in Figure 5.8.

To illustrate further the overdamped case, suppose that the damping ratio is increased to 5.0. Then the differential equation becomes $y'' + 20y' + 4y = 0$. With the same initial conditions used previously, the computer solution is as shown in Figure 5.9.

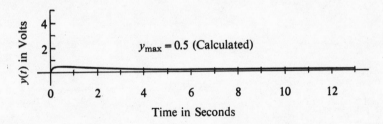

FIGURE 5.9. *The overdamped case, with $\zeta = 5.0$. Solution of the equation*
$y'' + 20y' + 4y = 0$, *with* $y'(0) = 10$, $y(0) = 0$.

Table 5.1 summarizes the results of the various illustrations, all of which had the same initial conditions and the same undamped natural frequency. The only differences were the values of the damping ratio chosen. It will be noted that the largest value of

TABLE 5.1. *Results of Variation of Damping Ratio*

Damping Ratio ζ	y_{max}	Actual Value of ω	Time to Reach Maximum Value
0	5.0	2.0 rads/sec	0.79 sec
0.2	3.8	1.96	0.70
0.6	2.5	1.60	0.58
1.0	1.8		0.50
2.0	1.1		0.38
5.0	0.48		0.23

y_{max} occurs when the damping ratio is zero. As the damping ratio is increased the value of y_{max} decreases, and the time required to reach the maximum value also decreases. This behavior of the value of y_{max} will be referred to in the following chapter in connection with the discussion of magnitude scaling.

VI

Magnitude Scaling

The fact that the output voltage of an operational amplifier becomes nonlinear outside a given range (± 100 volts for many computers) has already been discussed. In order to assure that this overloading of amplifiers causes no errors, problems are scaled so the magnitudes of all amplifier output voltages remain within the voltage range specified for the particular computer being used. This procedure is known as *magnitude scaling*.

There are two approaches to the selection of magnitude scale factors. In the first, which we shall call the "quick and dirty" method, the programmer patches up the problem on the computer, runs it, and measures the amplifier output voltages with a voltmeter. The voltages representing the dependent variables of the problem are then scaled down until all amplifier output voltages are within the operating range specified for the computer. This approach works very well for the majority of problems. It is not very elegant, but it gets the job done, and in most cases it is the results that count.

The second approach is more formal, and involves the analysis of the differential equations to be solved and the application of various accepted test methods to these equations. These methods require some understanding of differential equations and their behavior. Programmers who do not have this understanding will be obligated to acquire it somewhere along the way, and there is no time like the present to begin.

Before magnitude scaling can be accomplished, one must have

77

some idea of the probable maximum values which the problem variables will attain. Some scheme must be used to estimate these maxima, and such schemes are not widely published. Most books on analog computing show how to scale magnitudes in a problem, but they assume that one already knows one or more of the maxima, yet how these maxima were determined is seldom made clear. The books by Jackson and by Johnson do give some methods for estimation of maxima, and three such methods will be presented here. The use of the methods will be illustrated by example.

★ Method I. Second-Order Linear Differential Equations with Constant Coefficients

This method from Johnson [30] assumes that the damping ratio is zero, that is, there is no first-order term in the equation. As pointed out in the previous chapter, the solution of such an equation will be a sinusoid with a frequency of ω_n. Let the amplitude of this sine wave be K, then the solution is

$$y(t) = K \sin \omega_n t,$$

and the first two derivatives are

$$y'(t) = K\omega_n \cos \omega_n t$$

$$y''(t) = -K\omega_n^2 \sin \omega_n t.$$

Since the maximum values of the sine and cosine functions are 1.0, then

$$y(t)_{\max} = K \tag{137}$$

$$y'(t)_{\max} = K\omega_n \tag{138}$$

$$y''(t)_{\max} = -K\omega_n^2. \tag{139}$$

The fact that the method assumes a zero damping ratio, but can be applied to an equation which has a nonzero damping ratio, may bother the reader momentarily. If so, refer to Figures 5.4 through 5.9, or to Table 5.1. These show that the largest of the maximum values of the variable occurs when the damping ratio is zero. Thus Method I says, in effect, that for any second-order linear differential equation with constant coefficients, the maximum values of the dependent variable and its derivatives will never be greater than the maxima which are obtained from the same differential equation with the first-order term removed.

It should be pointed out that the maxima estimated by Method I agree best with the actual maxima when the damping ratio is between zero and 1.0, the region in which the transient solution is a sine wave. As the damping ratio increases beyond 1.0, the actual maxima become smaller and smaller fractions of the estimated maxima, and the prediction becomes progressively less accurate.

EXAMPLE

Estimate the maximum values of $y(t)$ and its derivatives in the following equation:

$$y''(t) + 2y'(t) + 5y(t) = 10 \cos t, \qquad (140)$$

with $y''(0) = y(0) = 0$ as the initial conditions. With zero damping, the equation becomes $y''(t) + 5y(t) = 10 \cos t$, for which the *transient* solution is $y(t) = K \sin \omega_n t$ (see Equation 130). The value of ω_n is the square root of 5, or 2.24. The value of K is now determined by applying the initial conditions. With $y''(0) = y(0) = 0$, Equation (140) reduces to $2y'(0) = 10 \cos 0 = 10$, whence $y'(0) = 5$.

The transient solution to the undamped form of Equation (140) is

$$y(t) = K \sin 2.24t.$$

By differentiating, $y'(t) = 2.24K \cos 2.24t$. At time $t = 0$, $y'(0) = 2.24K$. But $y'(0)$ has been shown to be equal to 5. Then $2.24K = 5$ and $K = 2.24$. By using Equations (137) through (139), the following estimated maxima are obtained:

$$y(t)_{max} = K = 2.24$$

$$y'(t)_{max} = K\omega_n = 2.24(2.24) = 5.0$$

$$y''(t)_{max} = -K\omega_n^2 = -2.24(5.0) = -11.2.$$

These maxima are the maxima of the transient solution of Equation (140) and its derivatives, assuming Equation (140) to be undamped. Method I states that, regardless of the damping actually present, these maxima will not be exceeded.

★ Method II. Second-Order Linear Differential Equations with Constant Coefficients

Jackson [31] gives this method, which assumes a zero damping ratio, zero initial conditions, and a forcing function which is a step function of magnitude A. The value of A is chosen to be the maximum value of the actual forcing function in the equation which is to be scaled. Such a step function is designated $Au_{-1}(t)$; it has the value of zero for all time less than or equal to zero and the value A for all time greater than zero. Figure 6.1 shows the graph of $Au_{-1}(t)$.

Given an equation of the form

$$a\frac{d^2y}{dt^2} + b\frac{dy}{dt} + cy = f(t), \tag{141}$$

the new equation from which the maxima will actually be estimated is

$$a\frac{d^2y}{dt^2} + cy = Au_{-1}(t), \tag{142}$$

since $b = 0$ (zero damping ratio assumed) and $f(t) = Au_{-1}(t)$ for the application of the method. With zero initial conditions, the

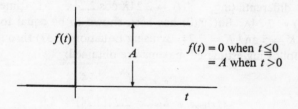

$$f(t) = 0 \text{ when } t \leq 0$$
$$= A \text{ when } t > 0$$

FIGURE 6.1. *The step function $Au_{-1}(t)$.*

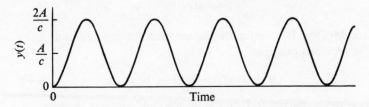

FIGURE 6.2.   *Graph of the solution of Equation (142).*

solution of Equation (142), stated without proof, is

$$y(t) = \frac{A}{c}(1 - \cos \omega_n t). \tag{143}$$

The graph of this solution is shown in Figure 6.2.

Figure 6.2 shows that $y(t)_{max} = 2A/c$, since the solution oscillates about the ordinate A/c rather than about the $y = 0$ axis. Successive differentiations of Equation (143) yield

$$y'(t) = +\frac{A}{c}\omega_n \sin \omega_n t$$

$$y''(t) = +\frac{A}{c}\omega_n^2 \cos \omega_n t.$$

Then the maximum values of the dependent variable and its derivatives are

$$y(t)_{max} = \frac{2A}{c} \tag{144}$$

$$y'(t)_{max} = \frac{A}{c}\omega_n \tag{145}$$

$$y''(t)_{max} = \frac{A}{c}\omega_n^2. \tag{146}$$

This method, like Method I, gives better estimates of the maxima if the damping ratio of the equation is between zero and 1.0.

EXAMPLE

Use Method II to estimate the maxima for the equation given in the previous example.

$$y''(t) + 2y'(t) + 5y(t) = 10\cos t, \qquad (140)$$

with $y''(0) = y(0) = 0$. Upon application of Method II, the equation becomes

$$y''(t) + 5y(t) = 10u_{-1}(t),$$

with $c = 5$ and $A = 10$. By using Equations (144) through (146), the maxima are found to be

$$y(t)_{\max} = \frac{2A}{c} = \frac{20}{5} = 4$$

$$y'(t)_{\max} = \frac{A}{c}\omega_n = \frac{10}{5}(2.24) = 4.5$$

$$y''(t)_{\max} = \frac{A}{c}\omega_n{}^2 = \frac{10}{5}(2.24)^2 = 10.$$

★ Method III. Nth-Order Linear Differential Equations with Constant Coefficients — The Equal-Coefficient Rule

For differential equations of second order or higher, the equal-coefficient rule may be used to estimate the maximum values of the dependent variable and its derivatives. This rule is an empirical relationship which involves normalizing the equation to obtain coefficients which are approximately equal. Jackson [32] discusses the method, the salient points of which will be given here.

Consider the nth-order differential equation

$$a_n\frac{d^n y}{dt^n} + a_{n-1}\frac{d^{n-1}y}{dt^{n-1}} + \cdots + a_1\frac{dy}{dt} + a_0 y = f(t). \qquad (147)$$

If each term of the equation is multiplied and divided by the maximum value of that term, the validity of the equation will not be affected. If we represent $d^n y/dt^n$ by $y^{(n)}(t)$, $d^{n-1}y/dt^{n-1}$ by

$y^{(n-1)}(t)$, and so on, Equation (147) becomes

$$y^{(n)}(t)_{max}a_n\left[\frac{y^{(n)}(t)}{y^{(n)}(t)_{max}}\right] + y^{(n-1)}(t)_{max}a_{n-1}\left[\frac{y^{(n-1)}(t)}{y^{(n-1)}(t)_{max}}\right] + \cdots$$
$$+ y^{(1)}(t)_{max}a_1\left[\frac{y^{(1)}(t)}{y^{(1)}(t)_{max}}\right] + y(t)_{max}a_0\left[\frac{y(t)}{y(t)_{max}}\right] = f(t).$$

The above equation is the normalized form of Equation (147). Method III involves assuming a step forcing function of the form $f(t) = Au_{-1}(t)$, and also zero initial conditions, as in Method II. The following steps are now taken in order:

1. Manipulate the coefficients of the bracketed terms so that they will all be approximately equal to A, the magnitude of the step function, except for the coefficient of the $y(t)$ term, which should be equal to $2A$. That is, set

$$y^{(n)}(t)_{max}a_n = y^{(n-1)}(t)_{max}a_{n-1} = \cdots = y^{(1)}(t)_{max}a_1 = A.$$

The coefficient of the $y(t)$ term should be adjusted so that $y(t)_{max}a_0$ is equal to $2A$.

2. The denominator of each term in brackets is now the maximum value sought for that particular term.

3. The maxima obtained in (2) above must either continually increase or continually decrease as the derivatives are taken in turn, that is, the maxima must constitute a monotonic set. If this criterion is not met, then the equal-coefficient rule is not applicable to the equation at hand.

EXAMPLE

Use the equal-coefficient rule to estimate the maxima for the equation given in previous examples. Since the maximum value of the forcing function, $10 \cos t$, is 10, the value of A will be chosen to be 10. By using the step forcing function, and normalizing Equation (140),

$$y''(t)_{max}\left[\frac{y''(t)}{y''(t)_{max}}\right] + 2y'(t)_{max}\left[\frac{y'(t)}{y'(t)_{max}}\right]$$
$$+ 5y(t)_{max}\left[\frac{y(t)}{y(t)_{max}}\right] = 10u_{-1}(t).$$

Now make the coefficients of the second-derivative and first-derivative terms equal to A (10 in this case), and the coefficient of the $y(t)$ term equal to $2A$, or 20, while still preserving the actual coefficients of the original equation.

$$10\left[\frac{y''(t)}{10}\right] + 10\left[\frac{y'(t)}{5}\right] + 20\left[\frac{y(t)}{4}\right] = 10u_{-1}(t).$$

Then the estimated maxima, which are the denominators of the bracketed terms, are

$$y''(t)_{max} = 10$$

$$y'(t)_{max} = 5$$

$$y(t)_{max} = 4.$$

These maxima are indeed a monotonic set, decreasing as the derivatives are taken in turn. The method is therefore applicable to this equation.

★ **Comparison of the Methods Given for Estimation of the Maximum Values of the Dependent Variable and its Derivatives**

In the previous section, three methods were given for estimating the maximum values of the dependent variable and its derivatives. These methods were applied to an example equation and the maxima were calculated. The example equation was then solved on an analog computer, and the solutions which were obtained are shown in Figure 6.3. Table 6.1 allows a comparison of the

TABLE 6.1.   *Comparison of Estimated and Actual Maxima*

Method used	$y''(t)_{max}$	$y'(t)_{max}$	$y(t)_{max}$
Method I	−11.2	5	2.2
Method II	10	4.5	4
Method III	10	5	4
Actual Values	−7.5	5	2.5

estimated and the actual maxima and shows that all of the methods predicted a larger value for $y''(t)_{max}$ than was obtained. It will be

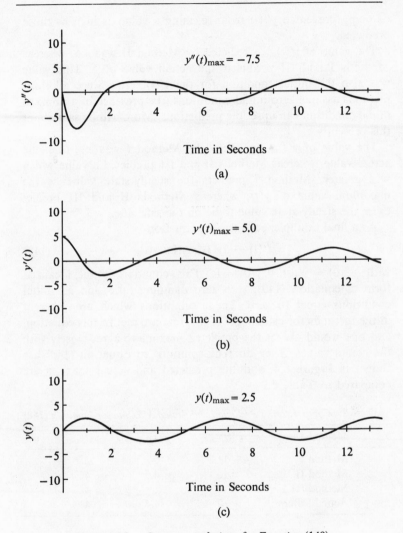

FIGURE 6.3. *Computer solutions for Equation* (140);
(a) $y''(t)$; (b) $y'(t)$; (c) $y(t)$.

remembered that two of the methods assume a zero damping
ratio, while damping *did* exist in the given equation. Thus, the

damping prevented $y''(t)$ from reaching a value as high as those predicted.

The value of $y'(t)_{max}$ predicted by Method II was 4.5, whereas Methods I and III predicted the actual value of 5. This value was also the initial condition for the $y'(t)$ term. Since all three methods assume zero initial conditions, the presence of a nonzero initial condition can upset the predictions. More will be said about this presently.

The value of $y(t)_{max}$ predicted by Method I was less than the actual value, whereas Methods II and III predicted a value which was greater. Method I predicts the steady-state value as the maximum value of $y(t)$, whereas Methods II and III predict twice the steady-state value to be on the safe side.

As a final example, consider the equation

$$y''(t) + 5y(t) = 10u_{-1}(t), \qquad (148)$$

with $y''(0) = y'(0) = y(0) = 0$. This equation is the idealized form of equation (140), with zero damping ratio and all initial conditions equal to zero. The assumptions which are inherent in the methods for estimation of maxima are met in this equation, and one would expect the predicted maxima to agree closely with the actual values. They do. The solutions to Equation (148) are shown in Figure 6.4, and the predicted and actual maxima are compared in Table 6.2.

TABLE 6.2. *Comparison of Predicted and Actual Maxima for Equation* (148)

Method Used	$y''(t)_{max}$	$y'(t)_{max}$	$y(t)_{max}$
Method I	−11.2	5	2.2
Method II	10	4.5	4
Method III	10		4
Actual Values	10	4.4	4

Methods II and III give the best value for $y(t)_{max}$ because they allow for the fact that the solution oscillates around the ordinate $y = 2$ instead of $y = 0$.

A comparison of Figures 6.3 and 6.4 shows the difference between the frequencies of oscillation of the two equations. In Figure 6.3, it

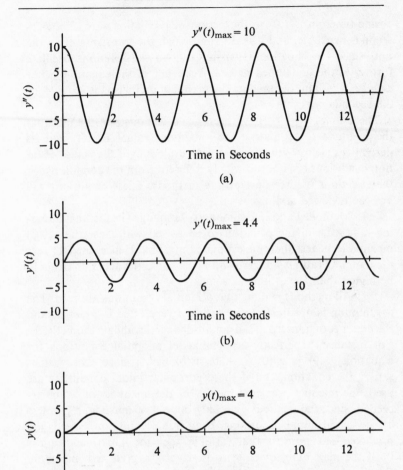

FIGURE 6.4.   *Computer solution of Equation* (148);
(*a*) $y''(t)$; (*b*) $y'(t)$; (*c*) $y(t)$.

is evident that after the transients die out the solutions oscillate at
the frequency of the cosine forcing function. The value of ω for this

cosine function is 1.0, so the period of oscillation should be 6.28 seconds per cycle, and it is. In Figure 6.4, the transients never die out, since the equation is undamped, so the solutions oscillate forever at the undamped natural frequency of the equation. Since $\omega_n = 2.24$ radians per second, the period of oscillation is $2\pi/2.24$, or 2.8 seconds per cycle.

The examples which have been given demonstrate the fact that the methods of estimating the maximum values of $y(t)$ and its derivatives yield results which are accurate only if the actual equation conditions are not too widely different from the conditions for the equations used to develop the methods. These conditions will now be reviewed and discussed.

1. Methods I and II assume zero damping. The fact that damping may exist in the equation to be solved will cause the actual maxima to be less than the estimated maxima. Hence, the fact that the damping ratio is not zero will never cause the actual maxima to be higher than the estimated values.

2. All methods assume that all initial conditions are zero. The assumption is not likely to be satisfied very often in practice, and the presence of nonzero initial conditions can invalidate the methods. For instance, a perfectly acceptable set of initial conditions for Equation (140) is $y''(0) = -30$, $y'(0) = 7.5$, since these values satisfy the equation. But if these particular initial conditions are used, the maxima predicted by any of the methods will *all* be exceeded, since the methods give only one set of maxima, regardless of the actual initial conditions. If an initial condition exceeds the predicted maximum for that variable, then the initial condition is itself the maximum, or close to it. Hence, a predicted maximum should always be compared to the initial condition for that term, and the larger of the two values taken for the prediction.

3. In Methods II and III the given forcing function was replaced by the step function $Au_{-1}(t)$, with A chosen to be the maximum value of the given forcing function. It is obvious that a function such as $3e^{2t}$ has no finite maximum, so what value should be used for A? In such a case it should be decided how long a period of time will be covered by the computer solution. Then calculate the value of the forcing function at the end of this period of time, and use this value for A.

4. One other point deserves mention, and that is the possibility that the characteristic equation may have one or more positive roots. The three methods given asume that the roots of the characteristic equation will have negative real parts, but if the real parts of one or more roots are positive, then the solution will "blow up"; that is, the solution will go to infinity with time. An unstable solution of this sort is easy to spot if the equation is second-order, because the coefficient of the first-order term will be negative, as

$$a\frac{d^2y}{dx^2} - b\frac{dy}{dx} + cy = f(x).$$

In equations of third order or higher, however, a positive root may exist even though the coefficients of all the terms are positive. The Routh criterion [33] may be applied here to check for stability of the solutions.

★ **Performance of the Magnitude Scale Change**

After having obtained estimates of the maximum values of the problem dependent variable and its derivatives, a magnitude scale factor must be chosen so that the computing amplifiers will not overload, and so that the recording of the computer solutions may be converted into terms of the problem dependent variable again for interpretation.

There are several ways in which computer variables may be related to problem variables in order to avoid amplifier overloading. One of the easiest to understand involves expressing the computer variable in volts, expressing the problem variable in its own physical units, and assigning a scale factor in volts per physical unit of the variable. For instance, suppose that the problem dependent variable is a flow rate having units of cubic feet per second. Then

$$Y = a_y y, \tag{149}$$

where Y is the computer variable, volts, y is the problem variable, cu ft/sec, and a_y is the magnitude scale factor, volts per cu ft/sec. This equation establishes the relationship between the problem variable and the computer variable. In order to limit amplifier output, the magnitude scale factor must be chosen so that the scale factor multiplied by the *maximum value* of the problem variable will not exceed the operating range of the computer. To illustrate, assume that the computer being used has an operating range of ± 100 volts, and that the maximum value of the problem variable is estimated to be 20 cu ft/sec. Then

$$100 = a_y (20)$$

$$a_y = 5 \text{ volts per cu ft/sec.}$$

Now that the magnitude scale factor has been estimated, Equation (149) can be rewritten as

$$Y = 5y.$$

The equation to be solved, which should already have been time-scaled, should now be rewritten, using the substitution $y = Y/5$ to give the *computer equation* in terms of Y and τ. Since the methods for estimating the maximum values of the problem variable and its derivatives are only approximate, the magnitude scale factor will probably not give exactly 100 volts for the maximum output of any amplifier. The estimated values will generally be higher than the actual values however, so that the maximum amplifier output is likely to be less than 100 volts, rather than greater. If the maximum amplifier output is found to be too small, a larger magnitude scale factor can be chosen and a new computer equation written. Of course, if some amplifier output exceeds 100 volts, then a smaller magnitude scale factor must be chosen.

★ Preliminary Computer Wiring Diagram

Before completing the magnitude scaling of a problem, it is advisable to make a preliminary wiring diagram to aid in visualizing the way the problem will be patched into the computer. With this preliminary diagram sketched out the amplifier outputs can then be analyzed and scaled to the proper values.

The first step in laying out the computer setup involves rearranging the equation to be solved so that the highest-order derivative appears alone on the left-hand side of the equation. Equation (140),

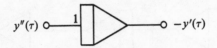

FIGURE 6.5. *Integration of $y''(\tau)$ to produce $-y'(\tau)$.*

which was used as a previous example, will be used again for purposes of illustration.

$$y''(t) + 2y'(t) + 5y(t) = 10 \cos t,$$

with $y''(0) = y(0) = 0$. The undamped natural frequency of this equation is 2.24 radians per second, which is slow enough to be handled easily by either a servoplotter or a galvanometer-type recorder. Thus the problem can be run in real time. By making the substitution $t = \tau$, and rearranging the equation, we obtain

$$y''(\tau) = 10 \cos \tau - 2y'(\tau) - 5y(\tau), \qquad (150)$$

with $y''(0) = y(0) = 0$.

Next, assume that $y''(\tau)$ is available as a voltage, and feed this signal into an integrator which has a time constant (RC product) of one. Then the output of this integrator will be $-y'(\tau)$, as shown in Figure 6.5.

Now feeding the output of the integrator of Figure 6.5 into a second integrator (also with a time constant of one) will produce $+y(\tau)$, as shown in Figure 6.6.

Thus, granting the $y''(\tau)$ is available for input to the first integrator, we see that $-y'(\tau)$ and $+y(\tau)$ can be generated as outputs. These outputs can be multiplied by the appropriate constants and algebraically summed with 10 cos τ to produce $y''(\tau)$. The $-y'(\tau)$ output must be multiplied by $+2$ and the $+y(\tau)$ output must be multiplied by -5 in order to produce the $-2y'(\tau)$ and the $-5y(\tau)$

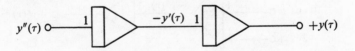

FIGURE 6.6. *Integration of $y''(\tau)$ to produce $+y(\tau)$.*

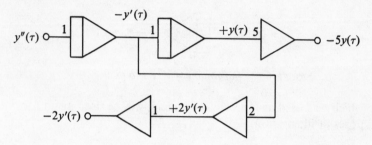

FIGURE 6.7. *Expansion of circuit to produce* $-2y'(\tau)$ *and* $-5y(\tau)$.

demanded by Equation (150). These operations are accomplished, and the setup now looks like Figure 6.7.

According to Equation (150), $y''(\tau)$ can be generated by adding 10 cos τ, $-2y'(\tau)$, and $-5y(\tau)$. However, the addition process will change the sign, and $-y''(\tau)$ will result from the summation, therefore an inverter (sign-changer) must be added to produce the desired quantity, $+y''(\tau)$. The generation of $+y''(\tau)$ is shown in Figure 6.8. The forcing function 10 cos τ shown in the figure can be generated directly on the computer (see Equations 87 through 90).

A complete circuit diagram for solving the given equation can now be prepared by combining Figures 6.7 and 6.8 and applying the proper initial conditions. The given equation had the initial conditions $y''(0) = y(0) = 0$; further, at time $\tau = 0$ the forcing function 10 cos τ has the value 10. Then at time $\tau = 0$, the equation becomes

$$0 + 2y'(0) + 0 = 10,$$

whence $y'(0) = 5$. This nonzero initial conditon for $y'(\tau)$ must be

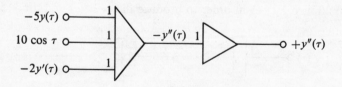

FIGURE 6.8.   *Generation of* $+y''(\tau)$.

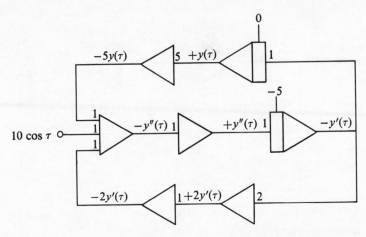

FIGURE 6.9.   *A computer setup for solving the differential equation*
$$y''(\tau) + 2y'(\tau) + 5y(\tau) = 10 \cos \tau.$$

applied to the first integrating amplifier, since it is this amplifier
which generates the function $y'(\tau)$. However, the output of the first
integrator is actually $-y'(\tau)$ (see Figure 6.5), so the initial condition
which should be applied is -5. The completed computer diagram
is shown in Figure 6.9.

The setup shown in Figure 6.9 is only one of many possible ar-
rangements for solving the given equation. It is not the most
efficient, however, and it is quite often necessary to conserve amplifiers so that the problem to be solved does not require more amplifiers than are available in the computer. After the operator has acquired familiarity with the capabilities of the various operational
circuits, he will be able to reduce the computer setup to the minimum number of amplifiers quite readily. For instance, a summing
amplifier and an integrator can be replaced by one summing
integrator. Also, a coefficient multiplier and a summer can be combined into one amplifier (with perhaps some coefficient potentiometers), since the summer can also be used to multiply. This last
fact can be used to eliminate two amplifiers from the setup in Figure 6.9 by removing the redundancy in the $-2y'(\tau)$ loop. A better
arrangement is shown in Figure 6.10.

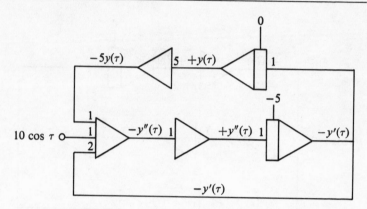

FIGURE 6.10. *Improved computer setup for solving the given equation.*

The smallest number of amplifiers, and hence the most efficient setup, can be obtained by reversing the polarities of the amplifier outputs and dispensing with the inverter which changes $-y''(\tau)$ to $+y''(\tau)$ in Figure 6.10. The resultant setup is shown in Figure 6.11. Note that the polarity of the initial condition must also be changed for the setup in Figure 6.11.

A final possibility will be given for solution of the problem which has been under discussion. It may not be necessary to observe the time behavior of $y''(\tau)$. If this is the case, then the summer and the integrator of Figure 6.11 may be combined into a summing-integrator. The resulting computer setup will thus require one less

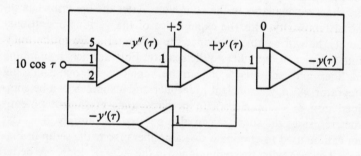

FIGURE 6.11. *Best computer setup for solving the given equation.*

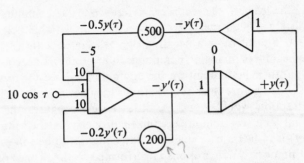

FIGURE 6.12. *Most efficient computer setup for solving given equation without displaying $y''(\tau)$.*

amplifier than the setup of Figure 6.11, but there is an additional advantage. It will be remembered that the maximum value of $y''(t)$ was predicted to be greater than the maximum values of either $y'(t)$ or $y(t)$ (see Table 6.1). If $y''(t)$ is not required, then it need not appear at the output of an amplifier, and it need not be considered in the magnitude scaling process. The ± 100 volts restriction on the operating range of the amplifiers applies to the amplifier *output* voltage. There is no similar restriction on the input voltage, and the amplifiers can take any *reasonable* input voltage, say 500 volts, without introducing inaccuracies in the solution or being damaged. Thus, omission of $y''(\tau)$ at an amplifier output conserves an amplifier and simplifies problem preparation. The resulting computer setup is shown in Figure 6.12.

The reader's attention is called to the fact that there is an odd number of amplifiers in each closed-loop path in the setups of Figures 6.9 through 6.12. An odd number of amplifiers should always occur in every closed computing loop if the computer solution is stable, that is, if the characteristic equations of the differential equations being programmed have no positive roots. If the solution is unstable, then loops with an even number of amplifiers will occur.

No attempt has been made in preparing these computer diagrams to cause the dependent variable and its derivatives to appear with positive signs only. Most recorders suitable for use with analog computers will accept either positive or negative signals, and in any event, the polarity of the signal can always be reversed by simply reversing the leads to the recorder. Reference to the computer diagram will always tell the operator whether the variable being recorded has a positive or a negative sign associated with it.

Many beginners in analog computation are rather amazed when they set up their first circuit on the computer and see the answers being recorded before their eyes. Perhaps they never really believed the contraption would work! A little reflection causes them to realize that a correct computer setup (if properly patched into the computer) is in fact a true analog of the equation to be solved; the required number of integrations is performed in the proper order, the dependent variable and its derivatives are multiplied by the prescribed coefficients, the various terms are provided with their proper algebraic sign, and the correct forcing function is applied. An infinite number of solutions to the equation is still possible, since the constants of integration have not been specified, but the solutions *must* be solutions to the given equation. When a particular set of initial conditions is chosen and applied, however, then there is one and only one possible solution for the dependent variable and each of its derivatives — there are no degrees of freedom remaining, and a unique solution is forced.

★ Systematic Procedure for Magnitude Scaling

In order to systematize the magnitude scaling procedure, the following steps should be taken in the order given. Assume the equation has already been time scaled, the maximum values of the problem variable and its derivatives have been estimated, and a preliminary computer setup has been sketched.

1. Study the computer setup diagram to determine which amplifier output will be the largest. This should be readily apparent, since the estimate of the maximum values of the dependent variable and its derivatives is at hand, and the computer setup shows the constants by which these variables have been multiplied.

2. Estimate the value of the output of the amplifier located in (1) above. This will be the estimated maximum value of the variable times whatever constants by which the variable has been multiplied, and the units will be the given physical units of the variable. For convenience, call this quantity m.

3. Determine the operating range of the computer being used. Call this voltage M.

4. Determine the magnitude scale factor a_y from the following equation:

$$M = a_y m.$$

This value of a_y is the magnitude scale factor of Equation (149).

5. Make the substitution $y = Y/a_y$ in the equation to be solved, which should already have been time scaled. The substitution should also be made in the initial conditions of the equation. The resulting equation, written in terms of Y and τ, is called the *computer equation*.

6. Rewrite the computer equation so that the highest-order derivative appears alone on the left-hand side of the equation with a numerical coefficient of 1.0.

7. Alter the computer diagram to take the new magnitude scale factor into account. This should involve changing *only* the initial condition voltages on the integrators and the magnitude of the forcing function.

8. Patch up the problem on the computer, make a static check to be sure that the voltages on the integrators at zero time agree with the altered computer setup, and run the problem. If one or more of the amplifiers overloads, measure the outputs with a vacuum-tube voltmeter to determine the maximum voltages.

9. Adjust the magnitude scale factor, keeping in mind that the amplifier output becomes nonlinear beyond the operating range, and the voltage output of an overloaded amplifier is somewhat lower than it would be if operation continued to be linear. Repeat steps (5) through (8) until the problem runs without overloading any amplifiers.

To illustrate the process, let us use our well-worn example problem, Equation (140). By using the equal-coefficient rule, the maxima of the equation were estimated to be

$$y''(\tau)_{\max} = 10$$

$$y'(\tau)_{\max} = 5$$

$$y(\tau)_{\max} = 4.$$

Reference to Figure 6.11 shows that no amplifier has an output whose absolute value is greater than 1.0 times the value of the variable or its derivatives. Then the maximum amplifier output will be the output of the summing amplifier, and this output will be proportional to $y''(\tau)_{\max} = 10$ in whatever physical units $y''(\tau)$ has.

Assume that the operating range of the computer being used is ± 100 volts. Then $M = a_y m$ becomes $100 = 10a_y$, whence $a_y = 10$ volts per physical unit of $y''(\tau)$. Equation (149) thus becomes $Y = 10y$.

The time-scaled form of Equation (140) is Equation (150), which is reproduced here.

$$y''(\tau) = 10 \cos \tau - 2y'(\tau) - 5y(\tau).$$

The substitution $y = Y/10$ in Equation (149) yields

$$\frac{Y''(\tau)}{10} = 10 \cos \tau - \frac{2}{10}Y'(\tau) - \frac{5}{10}Y(\tau). \tag{151}$$

To make the coefficient of the $Y''(\tau)$ term equal to 1.0, multiply both sides of the equation by 10. Then

$$Y''(\tau) = 100 \cos \tau - 2Y'(\tau) - 5Y(\tau). \tag{152}$$

The initial conditions must also be scaled. If $y''(0) = y(0) = 0$, then obviously $Y''(0) = Y(0) = 0$. The initial value of $y'(\tau)$ was previously found to be 5. By making the substitution $y = Y/10$, $y'(0) = Y'(0)/10 = 5$, and the scaled value of the initial condition is $Y'(0) = 50$ volts. Notice that this is the first time that the word "volts" has been associated with the values of the initial conditions. The magnitude scale factor changes the units of the initial conditions from the physical units associated with the variables to units of volts. Note also that, in performing the magnitude scale change, only the forcing function and the initial conditions were changed. The equation still has the same undamped natural frequency and the same damping ratio as Equation (140).

Equation (152) and the scaled values of the initial conditions constitute the computer equation for Equation (140). Now what do the predicted maxima look like? By using the equal-coefficient rule,

$$100 \left[\frac{Y''(\tau)}{100} \right] + 100 \left[\frac{Y'(\tau)}{50} \right] + 200 \left[\frac{Y(\tau)}{40} \right] = 100u_{-1}(\tau).$$

The new maxima are estimated to be

$$Y''(\tau)_{max} = 100 \text{ volts}$$

$$Y'(\tau)_{max} = 50 \text{ volts}$$

$$Y(\tau)_{max} = 40 \text{ volts.}$$

The first estimate of the magnitude scale factor is now complete. The computer setup of Figure 6.11 must be altered in two respects: first, the forcing function must be changed to $100 \cos \tau$; and second, the initial condition voltage for the first integrator must be assigned a value of $+50$ volts.

The problem must now be set up on the computer and run, to see if any of the amplifiers will overload. This was done, and none of the amplifiers overloaded, so no adjustment of the magnitude scale factor was necessary. The solutions to this problem were presented in Figure 6.3, except that the ordinate scale was converted to terms of y by applying the relationship $y = Y/10$.

★ **Alternate Magnitude Scaling Technique**

There is another magnitude scaling technique which is useful upon occasion. It sometimes happens that some of the variables in a problem have maximum values near zero, while the others have normal values. As a result, the outputs of the amplifiers operating on these low-valued variables are small, and drift and noise in the amplifier may partially obscure the voltage representing the variable. Further, it does not help to multiply the low amplifier outputs by some constant in order to magnify the output voltage, because the noise voltages are magnified by the same factor.

To avoid this difficulty, the equation may be rearranged so that the outputs of the amplifiers producing the variable and its derivatives will all be in the neighborhood of the maximum linear output voltage of the computer being used. The technique will be demonstrated by means of a numerical example.

Assume that the following equation is to be solved:

$$g''(t) + 2g'(t) + 50g(t) = 0, \tag{153}$$

with $g'(0) = 0$ and $g(0) = 0.5$. The undamped natural frequency is 7.07 radians per second, and the damping ratio is 0.14. A galvanometer-type recorder will be used, so no time scaling is required, and $t = \tau$. Method I will be used for estimating the maxima, and the solution will be assumed to be of the form

$$g(\tau) = K \sin \omega\tau. \tag{154}$$

Then the first derivative will be

$$g'(\tau) = K\omega \cos \omega\tau. \tag{155}$$

Upon application of the given initial conditions, Equation (154) gives $g(0) = 0.5 = K$ times zero, and Equation (155) gives $0 = K\omega$. The first result is nonsense, since it states that K multiplied by zero is not zero, and the second result is anomalous, since $K\omega = 0$ implies that either K or ω must be zero, yet neither case will give a solution for $g(\tau)$. Therefore, the solution must actually be a cosine function, or

$$g(\tau) = K \cos \omega\tau, \tag{156}$$

for which the first derivative will be

$$g'(\tau) = -K\omega \sin \omega\tau, \tag{157}$$

and the second derivative will be

$$g''(\tau) = -K\omega^2 \cos \omega\tau. \tag{158}$$

At time $\tau = 0$, Equation (156) gives $g(0) = 0.5 = K$. Then the estimated maxima are

$$g(\tau)_{max} = K = 0.5$$
$$g'(\tau)_{max} = -K\omega = -0.5(7.07) = -3.54$$
$$g''(\tau)_{max} = -K\omega^2 = -0.5(50) = -25.$$

If a magnitude scale factor of 4 volts per physical unit of g is used, then the estimated amplifier outputs will be

$$G(\tau)_{max} = 2 \text{ volts}$$
$$G'(\tau)_{max} = -14 \text{ volts}$$
$$G''(\tau)_{max} = -100 \text{ volts}.$$

The 2-volt output may be noisy, depending upon the quality of the computer being used. However, even if it is not, it will be difficult to determine the value of $G(\tau)$ accurately if it is read on the same scale as the value of $G''(\tau)$. Instead, let us try to scale up the amplifier outputs so that all of them will be around 100 volts. Since $g(\tau)_{max}$ is expected to be about 0.5, the amplifier output for this variable should be about 200 $g(\tau)$. Similarly, $g'(\tau)_{max}$ and $g''(\tau)_{max}$ are expected to be about 3.5 and 25 respectively, therefore the amplifier outputs for these quantities should be about 25 $g'(\tau)$ and 4 $g''(\tau)$ respectively. By rearranging Equation (153) to include these factors while still preserving the original coefficients, we obtain

$$\tfrac{1}{4}[4g''(\tau)] + \frac{1}{12.5}[25g'(\tau)] + \tfrac{1}{4}[200g(\tau)] = 0. \qquad (159)$$

If we multiply through by four and rearrange the equation to place the second-order term alone on the left-hand side, then we obtain

$$4\,g''(\tau) = -0.320[25\,g'(\tau)] - 200\,g(\tau). \qquad (160)$$

The above equation has the same undamped natural frequency and the same damping ratio as Equation (153), so the rearrangement has not really changed the original equation. The new initial condi-

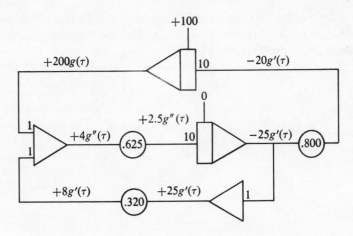

FIGURE 6.13.   *Computer setup for solution of Equation (153).*

tions are 200 $g(0)$ = 200 (0.5) = 100 volts and 25 $g'(0)$ = 0 volt·
The computer setup for solving the equation is shown in Figure 6.13·

It is a wise idea to check the output of the amplifier producing
4 $g''(\tau)$, since it might be in excess of 100 volts at time τ = 0. The
initial conditions for Equation (160) are 200 $g(0)$ = 100 volts and
25 $g'(0)$ = 0 volt. Upon substituting these values into the equation,
4 $g''(0)$ is found to be equal to -100 volts. Then none of the initial
conditions for Equation (160) are outside of the computer operating
range, and the computer setup shown in Figure 6.13 is ready to be
patched into the computer. The computer solutions actually obtained were 200 $g(\tau)_{max}$ = 100 volts, 25 $g'(\tau)_{max}$ = -74 volts, and
4 $g''(\tau)_{max}$ = -100 volts. These actual maximum values of the
dependent variable and its derivatives are compared with the predicted maxima in Table 6.3.

TABLE 6.3. *Comparison of Actual and Predicted Maxima for Equation* (153)

Variable	Predicted Value	Actual Value
$g(\tau)_{max}$	0.5	0.5
$g'(\tau)_{max}$	-3.5	-3.0
$g''(\tau)_{max}$	-25	-25

None of the maxima exceeds 100 volts, so no further adjustments
need be made in the computer setup, and the final computer solutions may now be recorded.

VII

Commercially Available
Analog Computers

The preceding chapters have discussed analog computers from the standpoints of theory of operation, mathematical operations which they can perform, and scaling. This chapter will describe four commercially available computers costing under $10,000. These four are representative of the large number of computers available, and it would be quite impractical to give an exhaustive listing.

HEATH COMPANY

The Heathkit Model EC-1 Educational Analog Computer is manufactured by the Heath Company, Benton Harbor, Michigan. The computer is shown in Figure 7.1. It costs $199.95, and there is a discount for educational institutions.

The computer contains nine unstabilized dc operational amplifiers having a dc gain of approximately 1000. Frequency response is down one decibel at 600 cycles per second. Amplifier output is -60 to $+60$ volts with load current up to 0.7 milliampere. The amplifiers are manually balanced by screwdriver adjustments mounted on the front panel.

The panel meter is a 50-0-50 microampere movement calibrated to read ± 1, ± 10, and ± 100 volts. The meter may be used to read

FIGURE 7.1.   *The Heathkit model EC-1 educational analog computer*
(*By permission of the Heath Company, Subsidiary of Daystrom, Inc.*)

power supply voltage, initial condition voltages, output of any of
the nine amplifiers, and to indicate amplifier balance.

There are three ungrounded power supplies which are used to
provide initial condition voltages. Each of these supplies provides
0–100 volts (positive or negative) at 5 milliamperes.

A relay with four sets of contacts provides for applying initial
condition voltages and for resetting problems. Repetitive operation
is provided at rates of from approximately 0.1 to 15 cps.

There are five 100,000-ohm coefficient potentiometers with
terminals on the panel.

Also provided are patch cords and computing resistors and
capacitors. There are nine 100,000-ohm and nine one-megohm
precision resistors (1 percent), three 0.1 microfarad and three 1.0
microfarad mylar capacitors (5 percent), and two silicon diodes.
All computing components are mounted on plastic double plugs.

The computer is a kit, and must be assembled by the purchaser.

Assembly time is about thirty hours. A beginner can build the kit, but results are generally much better if a qualified person does the assembly work. One cold-solder joint can cause hours of trouble-shooting and a surly disposition!

The Model EC-1 computer is limited in capacity, since it has only nine operational amplifiers. Further, there are only two inputs per amplifier. Thus the addition of three voltages could require three amplifiers; one for summing two of the voltages, a second for changing the sign of the first amplifier's output, and a third for adding the third voltage to the output of the second amplifier. As a result one is limited to rather simple problems.

The accuracy of the computer is also limited. This is understandable, since the open-loop dc gain is only about 1000. Still, as its name implies, the Model EC-1 Educational Analog Computer is designed to teach beginners, and beginners should start with simple problems and need not be too concerned with accuracy. This computer is the least expensive on the market by a wide margin, and is well worth the money.

The Heath Company formerly marketed a larger computer, the 15-amplifier Heathkit Group C. This was a much more flexible and more accurate computer, but it has unfortunately been discontinued.

SYSTRON-DONNER CORPORATION

The Donner Model 3400 analog computer is one of the computers manufactured by the Donner Division of Systron-Donner Corporation, 888 Galindo Street, Concord, California. This computer is shown in Figure 7.2 and costs $3,000 as pictured. There is no educational discount.

The computer contains ten chopper-stabilized amplifiers having a dc gain greater than fifty million. The stabilizing section declines in gain as frequency increases, becoming completely inoperative at about 5 cps. Beyond 5 cps, the frequency response is linear within ± 0.1 db to 4000 cps, and within ± 3 db to 50,000 cps. The phase shift of a unity inverter is less than 0.5 degree at 1000 cps.

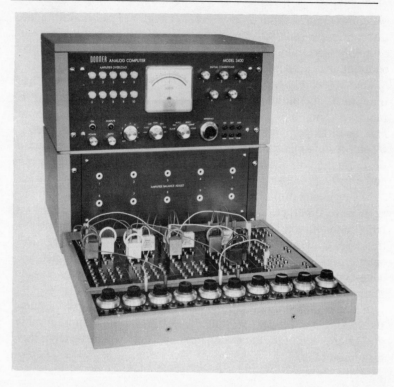

FIGURE 7.2.   *The Donner model* 3400 *basic desk-top analog computer*
(By permission of the Systron-Donner Corporation).

The amplifier outputs are linear from -100 volts to $+100$
volts at a current of 13 milliamperes. Drift of a unity integrator is
less than 0.1 millivolt per second. When necessary the amplifiers
may be balanced by screwdriver adjustments located on the front
panel, and balancing is very easy.

A multiple-position switch on the operating panel allows the
output of any amplifier to be displayed on the panel voltmeter.
This amplifier output is also made available at a pair of jacks on
the panel, so that the amplifier output may be recorded. The panel
voltmeter is of very good quality and has four ranges: ± 3.0 volts,
± 10 volts, ± 30 volts, ± 100 volts. This voltmeter is also used to

measure initial condition voltages, amplifier balance, output of coefficient potentiometers, or any other static voltage. A null comparator using a reference voltage and a ten-turn reference potentiometer allows voltages to be measured to within 0.1 volt.

The overloading of amplifiers is signalled by overload lights which are plainly visible on the control panel. These lights are numbered, making the detection of an overloaded amplifier a simple matter..

The computer contains ten amplifiers, five of which may be used as integrators. These amplifiers contain vacuum tubes, and a warm-up time of about 15 minutes is required.

There are five continuously variable initial condition voltage supplies from 0 to ±100 volts, and these are very easy to set. By using the null voltmeter, these voltages can be set to 0.1 volt. Internal relays are provided for integration, problem reset, and operation in the HOLD mode. Repetitive operation is provided, and the repetition rate can be varied over the range of one to ten repeats per second by means of a knob on the control panel.

The computer operational modes are RESET, COMPUTE, HOLD, AUTOMATIC (repetitive), SLAVE, and BALANCE. The SLAVE mode is provided so that two or more computers may be coupled together for increased capacity. One of the computers serves as the control station and the others are put in SLAVE mode.

Problem boards are detachable, and one is provided with the $3,000 package. Extra boards cost $150 each, and allow one to patch a problem up on a spare board while someone else is running a problem on the computer. Also, important or frequently used programs may be stored intact. The board itself is open and easy to use. The amplifiers have an adequate number of inputs for most problems; four of the integrating amplifiers and four of the summers have four inputs each, and one integrating amplifier and one summer have five inputs each. The color coding scheme is attractive and easy to understand.

A potentiometer strip providing ten coefficient potentiometers is supplied. Figure 7.2 shows the precision pot strip, which contains ten-turn, wire-wound potentiometers. A pot strip having single-turn potentiometers is available for less precise work.

Four component groups are available for use with the computer. These consist of patch cords and plug-in resistors and capacitors. Selections A and B include 1 percent resistors (deposited carbon) and 0.1 percent capacitors (polystyrene), with Selection B containing the larger variety. Selections C and D have 0.1 percent resistors (wire-wound) and 0.1 percent capacitors. Selection D offers the larger variety. The $3,000 package contains Component Selection B.

The manufacturer also offers nonlinear equipment to be used with the Model 3400 computer. An arbitrary function generator is available which approximates a desired function with 24 straight-line segments. Three types of electronic multipliers may be obtained: a single-channel, quarter-square type is available in plug-in version, etched circuit card version, and switch assembly version; a two-channel multiplier, available in modular or rack-mount version; and a high-accuracy, two-channel multiplier. A dual-channel transport delay generator is also offered, the standard range of dead times being 0.5 to 10.0 seconds.

The basic computer (see Figure 7.2) occupies a desk-top area 21 inches wide by 29 inches deep, and the height of the cabinet is 19 inches. If the desk-top unit is expanded by the addition of nonlinear equipment, such as the arbitrary function generator, the height of the unit is increased by the height of the function generator module, but the desk-top area remains unchanged. The basic computer and nonlinear auxiliaries may also be obtained in rack-mount form, and a floor-based installation is available at extra cost. The basic desk-top unit requires no extra cooling, but the expanded desk-top unit or rack-mount unit and the floor-based unit require cooling fans.

The Donner Model 3400 is a very satisfactory computer. It has many good features and is easy to use. Colleagues possessing this equipment report few maintenance troubles.

APPLIED DYNAMICS, INC.

An extensive line of analog computers is manufactured by Applied Dynamics, Inc., 2275 Platt Road, Ann Arbor, Michigan.

FIGURE 7.3. *The AD-2-24 PB analog computer with auxiliary X-Y plotter (By permission of Applied Dynamics, Inc.).*

Their smallest computer is the AD-2-24PB, which is shown in Figure 7.3. This computer costs about $9,000 as pictured, and educational institutions are allowed a discount. The components included are one prewired cabinet, one power supply, 24 stabilized amplifiers (eight integrator-summers, eight summers, and eight summer-inverters), 20 coefficient potentiometers (five with calibrated, locking dials), one high speed repetitive operation control unit, four dual repetitive reset units, one patchboard, and one patchcord kit.

The computer is expandable, and need not be purchased as shown. For instance, one can obtain the basic unit (prewired cabinet, power supply, control unit, twenty uncalibrated coefficient potentiometers, and patchboard and cord kit) and one unstabilized eight-amplifier integrator-summer module for about $5,000. The unit can then be expanded as need develops and funds permit. A variety of nonlinear equipment is also available, about which more will be said later.

The stabilized amplifiers have an open-loop dc gain of two

hundred million. The frequency response of a unity inverter is down three db at 80,000 cps, and the phase shift is 0.05° at 100 cps.

Amplifier output is linear from −150 volts to +150 volts, the current being 28 milliamperes at ±100 volts. Drift of a stabilized amplifier (referred to input) is 50 microvolts per day. Amplifiers are easily balanced by turning the balance-adjust knobs on the front of the amplifier modules until the neon light above the knob goes out. The amplifier offset is less than ±200 microvolts.

The output of an amplifier may be displayed on the panel meter by depressing the pushbutton corresponding to that amplifier on the front of the amplifier module. Amplifier outputs can also be continuously monitored on the meter by suitable patching on the problem board. Jacks are provided for external readout by oscilloscope, recorder, or digital voltmeter.

The panel voltmeter is of excellent quality and is protected against excessive current so that the meter will not be damaged even if several hundred volts are applied to it when it is on the one volt scale. The meter has four ranges for reading arbitrary inputs: ±1.00 volt, ±10.0 volts, ±100 volts, and ±500 volts. The meter selection switch has six other positions for checking computer power voltages and the reference voltage supplies.

Amplifier overload is signalled by neon lights on the front of the amplifier modules, so that detection of overloaded amplifiers is instantaneous.

Twenty coefficient potentiometers are provided. These are ten-turn, wire-wound potentiometers having wiper-arm fuses and readout pushbuttons. Figure 7.3 shows five of these potentiometers fitted with calibrated, locking dials. By using a null-potentiometer with a digital dial, these coefficient pots can be set to three significant figures between 0.0100 and 1.000. The pots are set loaded.

Computer operational modes are BALANCE, RESET, OPERATE, and HOLD. In BALANCE mode, amplifiers may be manually balanced to remove offset. In RESET the reset relays are energized, thus applying initial conditions to all integrators. In OPERATE all relays are released and integration proceeds on all integrators. In the HOLD position the hold relays are energized, disconnecting the inputs from all integrators and causing the solution to freeze in its current condition. The turning of the switch back to OPERATE causes the solution to proceed from the point at which it was halted.

Two or more computers may be slaved together to provide greater capacity for large problems. All of the Applied Dynamics computers are compatible, so that, for instance, two 24-amplifier AD-2-24PB computers could be slaved with one 64-amplifier AD-2-64PB computer. A PB-S1 slaving kit at $350 is required for each two computers in the enlarged system.

High-speed repetitive operation requires a Model 180 control unit and four Model 182 dual repetitive reset units. The latter are plug-in modules which replace the 0.1 microfarad capacitors normally used in the integrators with 0.01 microfarad capacitors. The repetition rate can be varied in six steps from one per second to 40 per second. The Model 180 control unit also provides positive and negative pulses to modulate the Z axis of a display oscilloscope; both period and amplitude of these time pulses may be varied. A positive pulse is available to trigger externally the display oscilloscope at the initiation of the reset cycle.

The problem boards are removable, and one is provided at the price quoted. Extra boards cost $55 each, and allow one to patch up a problem on a spare board while someone else is running a problem on the computer. Important or frequently used programs may be stored intact. The size of the patchboard is $6\frac{11}{16} \times 5\frac{5}{8} \times \frac{11}{16}$ inches, and this small size allows one to put it in a briefcase, or store a number of them in a desk drawer. However, this size can be a disadvantage to the beginner as the board is not as easy to understand as that of the Heathkit Model EC-1 or the Donner Model 3400. This board has great flexibility, however, and is representative of the type found on most larger installations. Once the layout is understood it is easy to use, and the color coding and labeling simplify patching and reduce patching mistakes.

All connections are made with patchcords. There are no external computing resistors and capacitors, these being mounted on circuit cards inside the computer; the patchcords are used to incorporate the desired elements in the problem circuitry. Computing components include 0.1 and 1.0 microfarad capacitors and 0.1 and 1.0 megohm resistors. All components have a matched accuracy of ±0.01 percent. Reset and hold relays are also internal, and are incorporated into the circuitry by suitable patching. There are four 0.1 megohm and four 1.0 megohm resistors per integrator-summer. This allows up to seven inputs for these eight amplifiers when used as summers (the eighth resistor is used as a feedback resistor), and up to eight inputs when the amplifiers are used as integrators. The eight multiplier-summers have three 0.1 megohm resistors and one 1.0 megohm resistor associated with them, any one of which may be used as the feedback resistor. The eight summer-inverter amplifiers have an internally wired 0.1 megohm feedback resistor and up to three 0.1 megohm input resistors. There are four outputs for each summer-inverter amplifier. All other amplifiers have five output connections.

Nonlinear equipment is also available for the Model AD-2-24PB. Included are quarter-square multipliers, dual X^2 diode function generators, dual log X diode function generators, combination sine-cosine diode function generators, diode networks, ten-segment variable diode function generators, and relay comparators. All of these components are interchangeable and are mounted inside the computer; access to them is provided by holes in the problem board.

The computer occupies an area $30 \times 20\frac{1}{2}$ inches and is 25 inches high. Expansion involves no extra space, as added nonlinear equipment goes inside the computer cabinet. The computer is also available in a form suitable for mounting in a 19-inch relay rack.

The AD-2-24PB is an excellent computer. It is easy to use, quite accurate, flexible, and maintenance problems are few.

ELECTRONIC ASSOCIATES, INC.

The PACE TR-20 analog computer is one of the computers made by Electronic Associates, Inc., Long Branch, New Jersey. The so-called "Basic TR-20" costs $4,350, and a liberal educational

FIGURE 7.4.   *The PACE standard nonlinear expanded TR-20 analog computer* (*By permission of Electronic Associates, Inc.*).

discount is allowed on this unit. Included in the basic unit are one prewired console (for full expansion), one power supply, one reference system, one overload indicator panel, one reference panel, five dual stabilized amplifiers (ten amplifiers), five dual potentiometers, carbon-film type (ten potentiometers), two dual integrator networks (allowing four of the amplifiers to be used as integrators), one display panel, one service shelf, one patchcord set, one multiple block, and two diodes.

The basic TR-20 is expandable by adding plug-in components, and a typical expansion is the Standard Non-Linear Expanded TR-20, known as the TR-20-2. This computer is shown in Figure 7.4 and includes the following components *in addition to* those already provided in the basic TR-20: five dual stabilized amplifiers, five dual potentiometers (carbon-film type), one quad potentiometer group, two dual integrator networks (allowing four more amplifiers to be used as integrators), three electronic quarter-square multipliers, one variable diode function generator (variable breakpoint, variable slope), one relay comparator, one function switch group, one high-speed repetitive operation group, one patchbay installation kit, one pre-patch panel, two patchcord sets, and two multiple blocks.

The price of the TR-20-2 is $11,356 expanded as shown. It is not necessary, of course, to expand from the basic TR-20 all the way to the TR-20-2; components may be added one at a time (or two at a time for those components available only as dual units) as the need arises. There is no discount for components purchased to expand the basic TR-20.

The open-loop dc gain of the stabilized amplifiers is thirty million. The gain of the stabilizing section decreases as frequency increases and becomes negligible at about 20 cps. The frequency response of a unity inverter is down three db at 300,000 cps, and the phase shift is $-0.01°$ at 100 cps and $-0.15°$ at 1000 cps.

The analog computers previously discussed had operating ranges of 100 volts or more. The TR-20 is a transistorized device, and its operating range is ± 10 volts. This does not mean that the computer is less accurate or less useful than the others; it just has a different voltage range. The other computers have three decades of usable voltage, these being 1 volt, 10 volts, and 100 volts. The TR-20 also has three decades, namely 0.1 volt, 1 volt, and 10 volts. Amplifier output is linear from -10 volts to $+10$ volts, the current at 10 volts being 20 milliamperes. Integrator drift with input grounded is typically 25 microvolts per second. The computing components include current guard circuits so that patching errors cannot damage the computer. For instance, unintentional grounding of an amplifier output has no adverse effect (except that it makes the resulting solution subject to question).

Amplifier balance is accomplished by turning the Meter Selector Switch to BAL and switching the Amplifier Selector Switch to the number of the amplifier whose balance is to be tested. The balance potentiometers for the amplifiers are located below the control panel and behind the snap-fit cover plate. If the panel voltmeter indicates a given amplifier needs balancing, the appropriate balance potentiometer is adjusted as necessary. The balancing procedure is easy, although somewhat more involved than with some other computers.

The output of an amplifier may be displayed on the panel meter by turning the Meter Selector Switch to AMPL and the Amplifier Selector Switch to the number of the amplifier whose output is to be monitored. This also makes the amplifier output voltage available at a jack on the control panel so that it can be displayed on an oscilloscope, a recorder, or a digital voltmeter.

The panel voltmeter is of very good quality. It may be used as a voltmeter, a null meter, or a balance indicator. When used as a voltmeter it has six ranges: ±0.10 volt, ±0.30 volt, ±1.0 volt, ±3.0 volts, ±10 volts, and ±30 volts. A nulling system employing a ten-turn potentiometer with a digital dial allows voltages to be read to three-place accuracy when the meter is used as a null meter.

Amplifier overload is signalled visually by the Individual Overload Indicator on the left side of the control panel, making the detection of overloading immediate.

Twenty-four coefficient potentiometers are provided in the TR-20-2, 20 at the top of the cabinet and four in the quad potentiometer group at the right-hand side of the control panel. The twenty coefficient pots located above the patch panel are ten-turn, uncalibrated carbon potentiometers. Wire-wound potentiometers with calibrated, locking dials may be substituted for the carbon pots for an additional $120 per network (one network contains two potentiometers). The pots in the quad coefficient group are the wire-wound, calibrated type. By using the panel meter (with its attendant precision potentiometer) as a null meter, the potentiometers can be set to an accuracy of 0.1 percent. The pots may be set loaded.

Computer operational modes are RESET, OPERATE, and HOLD. In RESET the outputs of all integrators are held at their specified initial conditions. In OPERATE all integrators are set free simultaneously, and integration proceeds. In HOLD the solution is frozen at any time that is convenient to the operator. The turning of the mode switch from HOLD back to OPERATE causes the solution to proceed from the point at which it was held, whereas switching back to RESET causes the problem to return to its initial conditions.

As many as six TR-20's can be slaved together to provide greater capacity for large problems. If two TR-20's are slaved together, all that is required is a slaving cable, costing $5.50. If more than two computers are slaved, one junction box at about $30 is required, regardless of the number of computers in the network, as well as a slaving cable for each slave computer. The PACE TR-48 computer is compatible with the TR-20, and may be added to the system (as long as there are no more than six computers in the network), but a slightly different slaving cable is required for the TR-48.

High-speed repetitive operation requires a rep op control panel (installed just to the right of the panel voltmeter) and Type 12.1115 repetitive operation integrator networks in place of the Type 12.1116 real-time integrator networks supplied with the basic TR-20. The price previously quoted for the expanded TR-20-2 includes the rep op control panel and the Type 12.1115 rep op integrator networks. The real-time integrator networks contain 10 microfarad capacitors, whereas the rep op integrator networks contain both 10 microfarad and 0.02 microfarad capacitors, allowing problem solution rates to be speeded up by a factor of 500. Solution time depends upon the time-scale factor used in preparing the machine equations, but repetition rate is determined by the setting of the rep op controls. The repetition rate can be varied in four steps from about two per second to about 30 per second, and the rate can be continuously varied between steps. The rep op control panel also provides a sweep voltage for synchronizing the computer with any standard display dc oscilloscope. A type 34.035 rep op display is available as an accessory.

The pre-patch panels are removable, and one is provided at the price quoted (the basic TR-20 does not include either the patch-bay installation kit or a pre-patch panel). Extra pre-patch panels for the expanded TR-20-2 cost $202 each, and it is recommended that three additional patchcord sets at $37.75 each be obtained with each extra pre-patch panel. It should be pointed out that the computer can be used without the pre-patch panel and the patch-bay installation kit. However, extra panels allow one to patch up a problem on a spare board while someone else is running a problem on the computer, and important or frequently used programs may be stored intact. The pre-patch panels are particularly useful in educational applications of the computer.

The pre-patch panels measure $12\frac{47}{64}$ inches $\times$ $16\frac{25}{64}$ inches $\times$ $1\frac{00}{64}$ inch. These panels contain color-coded plastic blocks which are identical in color and configuration to the faces of the components mounted in the computer proper. A set of spring contacts is mounted in the patching connections of the computer components, and when the pre-patch panel is locked onto the front of the computer, positive connection is made between the blocks in the pre-patch panel and the computer components. We are told by the manufacturer that the mechanism is quite reliable; contact trouble has been experienced in only one out of approximately 500 installations. The trouble was traced to some faulty spring contacts, and the computer performed properly when these were replaced.

The pre-patch panels are as flexible as the computer itself. If a particular problem requires a computing component which is not in the computer, the needed component may be substituted for a component which is in the computer but not being used. The components and their accompanying spring contacts are interchanged in the computer, and the plastic blocks are interchanged in the pre-patch panel. The possibility arises that someone may change a component in the computer and on his pre-patch panel, and some later user may not notice the change; upon plugging in his pre-patch panel (which agreed with the computer day-before-yesterday), he may obtain results which may astound him, or none at all. However, if one pays attention to business this should present no problem.

The substitution of pre-patch panel blocks is easily made, and while this sort of thing is not necessary with the computers which have been previously discussed, it can be classified as a minor nuisance only.

The layout of the pre-patch panel is not representative of that used on most larger installations, and the patching is not as easy to understand as is the case with some of the smaller computers. The scheme is logical, however, and once understood, the computer is easy to use. The color coding simplifies patching, and the fact that the pre-patch panel is larger than the removable problem boards supplied with most other computers should reduce patching errors.

Patching is done entirely with patchcords, as all computing resistors and capacitors are integral parts of the component networks. The resistors are wire-wound; feedback resistors have a tolerance of ± 0.05 percent, and input resistors are matched to these feedback resistors with a tolerance of ± 0.01 percent. There are five inputs to each operational amplifier used as a summer or inverter; two of these inputs prove a closed-loop gain of ten, and three provide a gain of one. There are also five inputs to each integrator, three with an RC product of one and two with an RC product of ten. All amplifiers are provided with five outputs.

Nonlinear equipment available for the PACE TR-20 includes variable diode function generators (both fixed breakpoint and variable breakpoint-variable slope models), log diode function generators, dual X^2 diode function generators, relay comparators for real time, electronic comparators for real time and rep op, dual function switches, quarter-square multipliers, and sine-cosine generators. Also available are a reactor kinetics network and a transport delay simulator.

The computer occupies a desk space 16 inches wide and 15 inches deep and stands 27 inches high. Addition of extra components requires no additional space.

The PACE TR-20 computer replaces the TR-10, which has become obsolete. The authors have not worked with the TR-20, but we are familiar with the TR-10, and we assume that the TR-20 is a worthy successor. The added convenience of removable pre-patch panels costs $273.50 for a patch-bay installation kit and $202 for each pre-patch panel, in the case of the expanded TR-20-2 (pre-patch panels for the basic TR-20 cost $95 each). This is rather expensive when compared to the cost of the removable problem board feature in other brands of computers. In other respects the TR-20 should be a very good computer. It should be easy to use, quite accurate, and should present few maintenance problems.

★   **Other Analog Computers**

A number of other firms market analog computers. Some domestic firms, together with their addresses and the name of the computer which they manufacture, are given in Table 7.1

Most of the computers manufactured by these companies cost more than $10,000.

TABLE 7.1. *Some Other Domestic Manufacturers of Analog Computers*

Firm Name and Address	Name of Computer
Berkeley Division Beckman Instruments, Inc. 2200 Wright Avenue Richmond, California	EASE
Comcor, Inc. 5310 East Pacific Place Denver, Colorado	CI-170
Computer Systems, Inc. Monmouth Junction, New Jersey	DYSTAC
George A. Philbrick Researches, Inc. 285 Columbus Avenue Boston, Massachusetts	Philbrick
Reeves Instrument Company East Gate Boulevard Roosevelt Field Garden City, Long Island, New York	REAC

VIII

Problems

A list of problems for general practice with the analog computer is difficult to assemble due to the wide variety of fields in which the computer is used. The problems presented here have been chosen at random from many fields; undoubtedly the reader will find many more in his own field of interest.

The problems have been arranged roughly in order of increasing complexity. The first few have many of the steps of solution indicated, the later ones are mere statements of the problem with an occasional hint or two. Scale factors will depend on the voltage range of the machine used and the type of readout equipment available.

1. Consider a body falling freely in a vacuum from a position of rest. The downward direction will be considered positive, and displacement will be measured from the rest position. The equation of motion of the body is

$$F = ma = mg,$$

where m is the mass of the body and g is the acceleration of gravity. The acceleration may be represented as

$$a = \frac{d^2y}{dt^2} = 32.2\frac{\text{ft}}{\text{sec}^2}.$$

The equation to be solved is then

$$\frac{d^2y}{dt^2} = 32.2,$$

120

with the initial conditions

$$y'(0) = y(0) = 0.$$

If a galvanometer type of recorder is to be used for recording the solution, a time scale factor of one second per second will be satisfactory. In this case computer time is equal to real time, or

$$t = \tau,$$

and

$$\frac{d^2y}{d\tau^2} = 32.2.$$

The choice of a magnitude scale factor depends on the time we wish to follow the motion of the body, since both distance and velocity go to infinity as the time becomes infinite. If we choose a magnitude scale factor of 10/32.2 volts per foot, we will be able to observe the body for a considerable distance (assuming a 100-volt machine).

$$Y = \frac{10}{32.2} y$$

and our equation becomes

$$\frac{d^2Y}{d\tau^2} = 10.$$

This is the machine equation, and the machine diagram is shown in Figure 8.1.

The initial conditions for the problem being $Y'(0) = Y(0) = 0$, we are ready to start the solution. Record both Y and $-Y'$ and compare your results with the analytical solutions of the original differential equation. Remember Y and Y' are machine variables

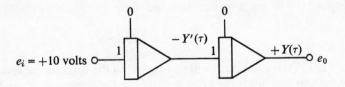

FIGURE 8.1. *Computer setup for solution of the falling body problem.*

and must be converted to problem variables by means of the scale factors employed.

If the body under consideration had not been at rest initially, but had been moving upward at a velocity of 50 feet per second, the initial conditions would have been

$$y(0) = 0$$

$$y'(0) = -50.$$

With the scale factors employed in the first part of the problem, the machine variable initial conditions would become

$$Y(0) = 0$$

$$Y'(0) = -50\left(\frac{10}{32.2}\right) = -15.5 \text{ volts.}$$

Notice that the output of the first integrator in Figure 8.1 is $-Y'(\tau)$. Thus, the initial condition voltage to be applied to this integrator is $+15.5$ volts. With these initial conditions run the problem again.

2. The analog computer can be used to generate many functions. As an example suppose we want a sine wave of amplitude 20 and an angular acceleration of 1 radian per second. We can use the computer to produce it.

$$f(t) = 20 \sin t$$

$$f'(t) = 20 \cos t$$

$$f''(t) = -20 \sin t = -f(t).$$

If we use a time scale factor of 1 second of computer time for 1 second of real time and a magnitude factor of 1 volt per unit amplitude, the machine equation becomes

$$\frac{d^2Y}{d\tau^2} = -Y.$$

What initial conditions will you use? Run the solution for several cycles and determine the average value for the frequency of oscillation. Determine the computer diagram for producing sin $2t$. What

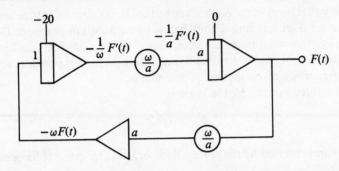

FIGURE 8.2. *Generation of sinusoidal function with variable frequency.*

changes would you make if sine waves of many different frequencies were wanted (see Figure 8.2)?

3. Use the computer to generate

(a) $$f(t) = 10 \sin 2t.$$

(b) $$f(t) = 25e^{0.1t}.$$

(c) $$f(t) = \cosh 0.5t.$$

4. A mass-spring-damper system is shown in Figure 8.3. Assume that the mass, M, is 10 slugs; the damping coefficient, C, is 200 lb sec/ft, and the spring constant, K, is 100 lb/ft. Assume

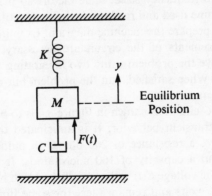

FIGURE 8.3. *The mass-spring-damper system.*

further that no external force is applied to the system and at time zero the mass is at rest and 1 foot below its equilibrium position. Determine the maximum distance above the equilibrium position reached by the mass, the time to reach this maximum position, and the frequency of oscillation of the mass.

The force exerted by the mass is

$$F_m = M\frac{d^2y}{dt^2}.$$

The forces exerted by the spring, damper, and any external force are

$$F_s = Ky$$

$$F_d = C\frac{dy}{dt}$$

$$F(t).$$

A force balance for the system provides the differential equation

$$M\frac{d^2y(t)}{dt^2} = F(t) - C\frac{dy(t)}{dt} - Ky(t).$$

Substitute the given values of the parameters in this equation and determine the expected maxima for y, dy/dt, and d^2y/dt^2. Determine the natural frequency of the system. From the expected maxima and natural frequency select scale factors so the problem will fit on the machine used and readout equipment available. Scale the equation, and prepare the machine diagram. Examine the diagram to see if all elements of the circuit are necessary. It should be possible to solve the problem using two integrating amplifiers and two summers. When satisfied, run the problem but do not neglect initial conditions.

5. An RLC circuit as shown in Figure 8.4 is to be examined to determine its transient behavior. It is anticipated that the actual circuit will have a resistance of 200 ohms, an inductance of 100 millihenrys, and a capacity of 100 microfarads. It is further anticipated that the voltage $E(t)$ will normally be 1 volt but occasionally will rise to 5 volts and remain there for some time. The circuit designer needs to know how long it will take for the capacitor to

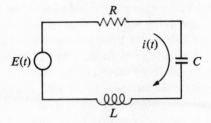

FIGURE 8.4. *The RLC circuit.*

charge to 4.5 volts when $E(t)$ does change to 5 volts. The maximum current in the circuit at any time would also be helpful in his design work. By using Kirchhoff's voltage laws, the differential equation relating charge to time is found to be

$$L\frac{d^2q(t)}{dt^2} = E(t) - R\frac{dq(t)}{dt} - \frac{1}{C}q(t).$$

The student should verify this equation, determine proper scale factors, make the machine diagram, and determine the things the designer needs to know. Recall that $dq/dt = i$, the current.

6. A group of animals exposed to a high dosage of gamma rays are observed to have varying resistivities to the effects of the radiation. They show an exponential survival characteristic; during the first day 25 percent of the animals die, during the second 25 percent of the remainder, and so on. It will be noted that the rate of death of the animals is a function of the number remaining. If the number of animals alive is called M,

$$\frac{dM}{dt} = kM,$$

where k is a constant. Use the computer to determine how long it will take for 99 percent of the animals to die. If you have to feed this group of animals, how many animal-days of food would you need? Program the computer so that 1 second of computer time is equal to 1 day of real time.

7. A sample of radioactive chemicals contains three different radioactive isotopes. Each isotope emits a gamma ray from each atom that disintegrates. The various isotopes disintegrate or decay

in an exponential fashion; in a period of time called the "half-life," one half of the remaining atoms of that isotope disintegrate. The first isotope has a half-life of 1 minute, the second a half-life of 40 seconds, the third a half-life of 30 seconds. At the time this sample of isotopes is first observed there are 10^8 atoms of each isotope. You are to determine the number of each kind of atom and the total number of radioactive atoms as a function of time. Determine the time it will take to reduce the radioactive atoms to 10 percent of the original total number. Program the computer so that the total population of radioactive atoms may be determined directly from the output of an amplifier.

8. A two-step chemical reaction is of interest to your firm. For security reasons the chemicals involved are designated by letters. The reaction may be written

$$R \underset{k_4}{\overset{k_1}{\rightleftarrows}} S \underset{k_3}{\overset{k_2}{\rightleftarrows}} T.$$

The reaction rate constants, k, are at present somewhat in doubt, so the solution must investigate the effect of various values for the different k's. Since the reactions are reversible, the effect of storage on product T is also to be investigated.

The differential equations expressing the change of concentration of each of the three materials with time may be written

$$\frac{dC_R}{dt} = -k_1 C_R + k_4 C_S$$

$$\frac{dC_S}{dt} = k_1 C_R - k_4 C_S - k_2 C_S + k_3 C_T$$

$$\frac{dC_T}{dt} = k_2 C_S - k_3 C_T.$$

In order to simplify the problem we will use normalized concentrations, C_S, C_T, C_R, varying between 0 and 1.0. Use a scale factor of 100 volts for a concentration of 1.0. Determine the concentration as a function of time for R, S, and T for the following conditions:

Initial Concentrations   Rate Constants

(a) $C_R(0) = 1$ $k_1 = k_2 = 1$

$C_S(0) = C_T(0) = 0.$ $k_3 = k_4 = 0.$

(b) $C_R(0) = C_S(0) = 0.5$ $k_1 = k_2 = k_3 = k_4 = 0.$

$C_T(0) = 0.$

(c) $C_R(0) = C_S(0) = 0$ $k_1 = k_2 = 0.5$

$C_T(0) = 1.0.$ $k_3 = k_4 = 0.2.$

(d) $C_R(0) = 0.75$ $k_1 = 0.75,\quad k_2 = 0.40$

$C_S(0) = 0.25.$ $k_3 = 0.25,\quad k_4 = 0.10.$

$C_T(0) = 0.$

9. A study of a proposed tank installation at your plant is to be made to determine the transient behavior of the flow from the second tank if the flow into the first tank is suddenly increased. The arrangement of tanks is shown in Figure 8.5.

The units of F, the flow, will be cubic feet per minute; the capacity, C, of the tanks is given in cubic feet per foot of depth; the height of fluid in the tanks, h, is in feet. The liquid flowing out of a given tank suffers head losses due to constrictions, fittings, piping, and valves. All of these losses are lumped into a single equivalent resistance, R, with units of foot minutes per cubic foot. This equivalent resistance

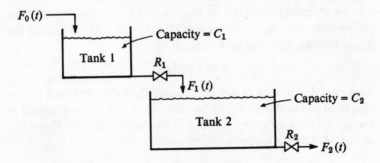

FIGURE 8.5. *Two-tank liquid flow process.*

is equal to the slope of the head versus flow curve in the region of interest. This curve is normally not linear, but in the interests of simplification we will assume it is straight in the region we are using, and the resistance may be treated as a constant.

The differential equations describing the system shown in Figure 8.5 are

$$R_1 C_1 \frac{dF_1(t)}{dt} + F_1(t) = F_0(t)$$

$$R_2 C_2 \frac{dF_2(t)}{dt} + F_2(t) = F_1(t).$$

These equations may be combined to eliminate F_1 and its functions.

Some simple measurements on the system give the following values:

$$R_1 = 0.1 \text{ ft min/cu ft}$$

$$R_2 = 0.2 \text{ ft min/cu ft}$$

$$C_1 = 5.0 \text{ cu ft/ft}$$

$$C_2 = 10.0 \text{ cu ft/ft.}$$

The system is in equilibrium at time zero with

$$F_0(0) = F_1(0) = F_2(0) = 0.50 \text{ cu ft/min.}$$

At time zero F_0 is increased to 0.75 cu ft/min and held at that value.

Determine F_1 and F_2 as a function of time.

10. A cylindrical tank of diameter D is emptied through an orifice with diameter d, on the side of the tank. The velocity of the liquid flowing from the tank is given by

$$v = C_0\sqrt{2gh},$$

where v is the velocity in feet per second, C_0 is the coefficient of discharge of the orifice and may be taken as 0.6 in this problem, g is the acceleration of gravity, and h is the height of fluid above the orifice. A material balance for the system gives

$$\frac{\pi d^2}{4} v = -\frac{dh}{dt} \frac{\pi D^2}{4}.$$

These two equations may be combined to eliminate v and yield a differential equation in h and t. If the tank is 2 feet in diameter and the orifice is 1 inch in diameter how long would it take to lower the level of the water in the tank from 30 to 10 feet above the orifice?

The solution of the problem on the analog computer requires a function generator or square root card.

11. If two function generators and a multiplier are available, solve Problem 10 if the tank is in the shape of a 30° right angle cone placed apex down. Assume the orifice is at the apex of the cone. A tank having a nonuniform cross-section makes D a function of h. In generating the function of h to be used in this problem pay particular attention to scale factors. We want to generate the scaled function of h rather than the function itself.

12. The analog computer can be used to solve partial differential equations. Since the computer integrates only with respect to time, the partial differential equations must be converted to a set of ordinary differential equations before the computer can operate on them. Suppose we have a large slab of material with an insulator on one face and a heat source which maintains a constant temperature on the other face. The thickness of the slab may be taken as L. We will assume the slab is large enough in the y and z directions to be considered infinite, so that temperature variations need to be considered only in the x direction, the direction perpendicular to the faces of the slab. The arrangement is shown in Figure 8.6.

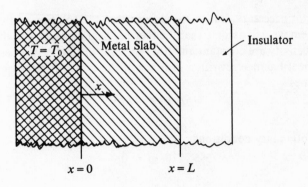

FIGURE 8.6. *Heat transfer in an infinite slab.*

If C is the heat capacity of the slab per unit volume and K is the thermal conductivity, the heat balance becomes

$$C\frac{\partial T}{\partial t} = \frac{\partial}{\partial x}\left(K\frac{\partial T}{\partial x}\right),$$

where T is the temperature of the slab at a point and a particular instant in time. The boundary conditions for the slab are

$$T(0, t) = 0$$

$$\frac{\partial T}{\partial x}(L, t) = 0.$$

The first boundary condition assumes that we can call the constant temperature maintained at the $x = 0$ face zero in our temperature scale. The problem becomes simpler if we use dimensionless time and space variables. Define a dimensionless space variable by

$$X = \frac{x}{L},$$

which leads to

$$\frac{\partial}{\partial x} = \frac{\partial}{\partial X}\frac{\partial X}{\partial x} = \frac{1}{L}\frac{\partial}{\partial X}.$$

Next a dimensionless time variable is defined by

$$\tau = \frac{Kt}{CL^2}.$$

It is not necessary, but to simplify further the solution of this first problem we will assume that the thermal heat capacity and thermal conductivity are constant and not functions of time or temperature. The heat balance rewritten in terms of the dimensionless variables becomes

$$\frac{\partial T}{\partial \tau} = \frac{\partial}{\partial X}\left(\frac{\partial T}{\partial X}\right)$$

with boundary conditions

$$T(0, \tau) = 0$$

$$\frac{\partial T}{\partial X}(1, \tau) = 0.$$

If the original temperature distribution within the slab can be defined by

$$T(X, 0) = T_0(X),$$

the heat flow is defined.

To solve the problem we assume the variables can be separated

$$T(X, \tau) = \mathbf{X}(X)\mathbf{T}(\tau).$$

By substituting into the heat balance equation we have

$$\mathbf{X}(X)\frac{d\mathbf{T}(\tau)}{d\tau} = \mathbf{T}(\tau)\frac{d}{dx}\left(\frac{d\mathbf{X}(X)}{dX}\right)$$

$$\frac{1}{\mathbf{T}(\tau)}\frac{d\mathbf{T}(\tau)}{d\tau} = \frac{1}{\mathbf{X}(X)}\frac{d}{dX}\left(\frac{d\mathbf{X}(X)}{dX}\right).$$

The left side is a function of time only, and the right side is a function of position only; to be equal for all time and all positions they must be equal to a constant. Let the constant be $-\alpha$. Thus

$$\frac{1}{\mathbf{T}}\frac{d\mathbf{T}}{d\tau} = -\alpha$$

and

$$\frac{d}{dX}\left(\frac{d\mathbf{X}}{dX}\right) + \alpha\mathbf{X} = 0.$$

The solution of the equation in time is simply the exponential decay equation

$$T = Ae^{-\alpha\tau},$$

where A is an arbitrary constant.

The boundary conditions we established will be satisfied only if

$$\mathbf{X}(0) = \frac{d\mathbf{X}(1)}{dX} = 0.$$

For these boundary conditions the equation in the space variable X can only be solved for discrete α values. These discrete values of α are called *eigenvalues*, and the corresponding $\mathbf{X}_n(X)$ solutions are called *eigenfunctions*. Once the eigenfunctions are determined the complete solution can be written as an infinite series

$$T(X, \tau) = \sum_{n=1}^{\infty} A_n X_n(X) e^{-\alpha_n \tau}.$$

The arbitrary constants A_n are determined from the original temperature distribution in the slab.

We want to use the computer to determine the eigenvalues. The equation in question is

$$\frac{d^2 X}{dX^2} + \alpha X = 0.$$

The boundary values are

$$X(0) = \frac{dX(1)}{dX} = 0.$$

Since the computer can differentiate only with respect to time, we let X correspond to time on the computer. In this manner the equation says we start with a value of $X = 0$ at time zero and end with a value of $dX/dX = 0$ one unit of computer time later. Such a condition will exist only for the values of α that are eigenvalues. A circuit is set up with variable α, and various α's are tried until such a solution is found. The values of α that give such solutions are eigenvalues.

In order to make the solution practical for the computer we pick some convenient interval of time for recording the solutions. If an X-Y plotter or galvanometer recorder is used, 5 seconds might make a convenient time. By making the time constant of each integrator 5 seconds, one unit of computer time becomes 5 seconds of real time. The potentiometers used to represent α must be varied over wide ranges. To make the potentiometer setting easy another factor is introduced, call it r^2, so that $r^2 \alpha$ becomes a value easily set on a potentiometer. A machine diagram to accomplish this is shown in Figure 8.7. Initial conditions are

$X = 0$

$\dfrac{dX}{dX} =$ arbitrary constant, make it as large as convenient with the computer used.

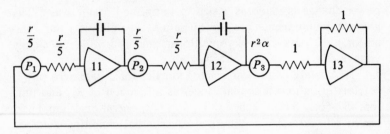

FIGURE 8.7. *Machine diagram for eigenvalue determination.*

The student should verify the computer diagram and, using this circuit, determine the first four eigenvalues.

13. Solve Problem 12, but allow the thermal conductivity to vary with distance in the slab. Let the thermal conductivity be

$$C = C_0(1 + 0.1X).$$

★ **Solved Problems in the Literature**

The following list, which is by no means exhaustive, gives sources and brief statements of problems which have been set up for solution on analog computers. Final computer programs are given for all problems listed. Approximate component requirements are given for each problem so that the reader will be able to tell whether the problem can be handled on the equipment available to him.

Bryant, L. T., L. C. Just, and G. S. Pawlicki, "Introduction to Electronic Analogue Computing," Argonne National Laboratory Report ANL-6187.

1. Sine-wave generator (pp. 48–50). The generation of a sine wave of amplitude b and angular velocity ω. This requires three operational amplifiers (two of them integrators), three potentiometers, and one initial condition voltage. If an X-Y plotter is used to write out the solution, add an integrator, a pot, and a 100-volt supply.

2. The analysis of iodine and xenon concentrations in a nuclear reactor as a function of time and neutron flux (pp. 51–59). The

power change is made as a step, a ramp, and a sine wave. The greatest requirements are 14 operational amplifiers (four integrators), 13 pots, one servomultiplier, and four 100-volt supply voltages.

3. A study of nuclear reactor kinetics for a bare zero power reactor (in its lowest spatial mode) as a function of K_{ex} and time (pp. 59–66). This problem requires 11 operational amplifiers (seven integrators), 34 pots, and seven initial condition voltages.

4. A demonstration of the production and consumption of fissionable isotopes in the fuel of a one-region fast reactor (pp. 67–80). This requires 38 operational amplifiers (12 integrators), 64 pots, four servomultipliers, and 12 initial condition voltages.

Bryant, L. T., M. J. Janicke, L. C. Just, and A. L. Winiecki, "Engineering Applications of Analog Computers," Argonne National Laboratory Report ANL-6319.

1. A study of Elias' equation for motion of a control rod in a reactor core (pp. 6–12). The motion is damped by a hydraulic buffer mechanism (dashpot). The relationships obtained are velocity of rod versus distance for various viscosities of hydraulic oil, velocity versus distance for various initial velocities, velocity versus time for various viscosities, and distance versus time for various initial velocities. The study requires six operational amplifiers (two of them integrators), five pots, three function multipliers, and three 100-volt supplies.

2. A study of MacFarlane's equation, which expresses the variation of pressure with distance through a packed-bed reactor (pp. 13–17). This requires nine operational amplifiers (two integrators), seven pots, three function multipliers, five voltage sources, and a high-speed differential relay.

3. The simulation of a reactor transient initiated by control rod withdrawal and terminated by the negative temperature coefficient (pp. 18–26). The equations describing the neutron kinetics (with six delayed groups) are solved on the computer. These equations are forced by changes in K_{ex}. The requirements are 24 operational amplifiers (nine integrators), 28 pots, three function multipliers, one diode function generator, two high-speed differential relays, and 13 voltage sources.

4. A vibrating system with two degrees of freedom (pp. 27–31). Two masses are suspended vertically by two springs, with the masses allowed to move only vertically. Wind friction, spring mass, and energy dissipation in the elastic springs are neglected. Seven operational amplifiers (four integrators), five pots, and two voltage sources are needed.

5. Temperature distribution in a radiating fin (pp. 32–36). An investigation of the rejection of heat from finned exchangers, to be applied to the cooling of outer-space power plants. The addition of fins to the tubes carrying the power plant working fluid reduces the number of tubes required, thus decreasing the probability of meteor puncture of the coolant-carrying tubes. This study requires three operational amplifiers (two integrators), two pots, two function multipliers, and two voltage sources.

6. Temperature distribution in an infinite slab of insulated zirconium, considering variable thermal properties (pp. 37–48). Four cases are considered:

(a) Diffusivity is a constant. This requires 12 operational amplifiers (six integrators), 16 pots, a high-speed differential relay, and eight voltage sources.

(b) Diffusivity is considered to be a function of the arithmetic average temperature. This requires 21 operational amplifiers (six integrators), ten pots, one high-speed differential relay, one diode function generator, one servomultiplier (with six connections), and seven voltage supplies.

(c) Diffusivity is a function of the temperature in the region described by the heat balance. This requires 27 operational amplifiers (six integrators), eight pots, four diode function generators, four servomultipliers, one high-speed differential relay, and seven voltage sources.

(d) Diffusivity is a function of the average temperature across an interface. Eighteen operational amplifiers (six integrators) eight pots, five diode function generators, five multipliers, one high-speed differential relay, and seven voltage sources are required.

Donner Tech Notes, publications of the Donner Scientific Company, 888 Galindo Street, Concord, California. Free on request.

Donner Tech Notes No. 1. The simulation of a positional

servomechanism. A shaft is controlled by a motor drive so that the shaft position always equals the input command signal. A voltage is derived from the shaft position and compared to the input command voltage. The difference between these voltages is amplified, and passed to the control field of an amplidyne. This generator voltage is applied to the d-c motor drive with constant field excitation. The system contains a nonlinearity in the form of backlash in the gears driving the potentiometer sensing the position of the shaft. Eight operational amplifiers (two integrators), nine pots, two diodes and two voltage sources are needed.

Donner Tech Notes No. 2.

(a) A simple suspended pendulum, with no damping and small angular displacement (to avoid nonlinear equations). This requires three operational amplifiers (two integrators), two pots, and one 100-volt supply. If an X-Y plotter is used to record the solution, add an integrator, a pot, and a 100-volt supply.

(b) The inverted pendulum with sinusoidal displacement applied at the point of support. The system is undamped and the angular displacement is kept small. A particular solution is obtained, and a stability analysis of the pendulum is made. Requires five operational amplifiers (four integrators), six pots, one function multiplier, and two 100-volt supplies.

Literature From Electronic Associates, Inc. PACE TR-10 Application Notes. These twelve problem sheets (problems outlined below) are available upon request from Electronic Associates, Inc., Long Branch, New Jersey.

1. Design of an Automobile Suspension System. An investigation of the response of an automobile suspension system (single wheel, simulated by two masses, two springs, and a dashpot) for selected disturbances. The most suitable values for the system parameters are determined by selecting the most desirable response from the computer solutions. This requires eight operational amplifiers (four of which are integrators), nine pots, and no constant voltage supplies.

2. Calculation of Heat Transfer by Natural Convection. The determination of the temperature and velocity distributions for various Prandtl numbers, and calculation of the heat transferred

from a vertical flat plate. The requirements are 14 operational amplifiers (five integrators), six pots, one dual X^2 diode function generator, two function multipliers, and two voltage supplies.

3. Calculation of Radial Velocity of a Rotary Spray Drier. The curve of radial velocity of a particle versus the radial distance from the center of the disk used in a spray drier is computed. The results are used to select the design parameters of a drier for a particular study. Requires seven operational amplifiers (two integrators), three pots, one dual X^2 diode function generator, one function multiplier, and one voltage supply.

4. Analysis of the Flow Path of an Oil Globule. A settler is used to separate an oil-water mixture. The overflowing level for the oil is 5 feet above the bottom of the oil retention baffle. The minimum length of the separation section of the separator is to be calculated. Four amplifiers (two integrators), three pots, a dual X^2 diode function generator, and one voltage supply are required.

5. Investigation of a Simple Chemical Reaction. Chemical component A reacts to form B, which in turn reacts to form C. The reaction rate for A to B is r_1 and for B to C is r_2. For isothermal reaction, find the concentration of A, B, and C with time for the case of $r_1 = 1.0$ and r_2/r_1 less than 1.0. This requires four operational amplifiers (three integrators), two pots, and one voltage supply.

6. Dynamic Response of a Separately Excited Generator. An investigation of the time response of a separately excited generator with constant resistive load, for various changes in the exciter voltage. Four operational amplifiers (two integrators), nine pots, and four voltage supplies are required.

7. Time Response of a Two-Winding Transformer. The determination of the time response of a particular design of two-winding transformer for changes in the resistive load and input voltage. This requires five operational amplifiers (one integrator), six pots, and one voltage supply for input.

8. Investigation of Unsteady-State Heat Conduction. A determination of the temperature distribution in the x direction for a long, wide slab which is initially at a high temperature and

then is suddenly quenched in an ice bath. It is assumed that the temperature in the slab varies only in the x direction. This requires 15 operational amplifiers (five integrators), ten pots, and five voltage supplies.

9. Investigation of the Reaction of Sodium Vapor Diffusing into a Halide. A study of the effects of changes in design parameters on the reaction of sodium vapor diffusing into a halide, where diffusion of the reactants and products controls the rate of reaction. A trial and error method of solution is necessary. Thirteen operational amplifiers (three integrators), eight pots, two function multipliers, and four voltage supplies are required.

10. Investigation of the Process Parameters Affecting the Control of a Stirred-Tank Reactor. A study of the effect of parameter changes on the time response of the output concentration of a steamjacketed, stirred-tank reactor. This requires ten operational amplifiers (two integrators), 13 pots, one function multiplier, and six voltage supplies.

11. Investigation of the Output Response of a Positional Servo System. A study of output response to input disturbances, with changes in the system parameters. Nine operational amplifiers (three integrators), nine pots, and two voltage supplies are required.

12. Investigation of the Response of a Nuclear Reactor. A study of the time response of a nuclear reactor with changes in the reactor multiplication factor. This requires 12 operational amplifiers (six integrators and one summer with seven inputs), 14 pots, one function multiplier, and one voltage supply.

PACE TR-10 Simulation Bulletins. These eight problem sheets (problems outlined below) are available upon request from Electronic Associates, Inc., Long Branch, New Jersey.

1. Simulation of a Spring-Mass System. A study of a mass-spring-damping system with initial displacement, to determine the response. Various values of damping, spring constant, and mass used. This requires three operational amplifiers (two integrators), three pots, and one voltage supply.

2. Dynamic Characteristics of a Distillation Column. A system for simulating the dynamics of a three-plate, single-com-

ponent distillation column. Provisions are made for changing the feed composition, the feed flow rate, the distillate flow, the vapor flow, the plate holdup, and the reflux ratio. This requires 16 operational amplifiers (seven integrators), eight pots, four servomultipliers, and four voltage supplies.

3. Simulation of a Tubular Reactor. The calculation of the required length of a tubular chemical reactor to obtain a specific composition for a range of input and operating conditions. Conditions varied include input gas temperature, furnace temperature, input feed rate, tube diameter, and viscosity of the gas mixture. This requires 18 operational amplifiers (four integrators), 21 pots, four servomultipliers, and five voltage supplies.

4. Chemical Reactor Problems. A simulation of the fixed-bed catalytic chemical reactor model of Wehner and Wilhelm. The model is of an isothermal reactor involving only axial diffusion and flow with a first-order reaction. A system of three equations is written describing reactant concentration in three zones: the foresection, the reactor itself, and the after-section. The computer solution requires six operational amplifiers (four integrators), six pots, two function switches, and two voltage supplies.

5. Simulation of a Pressure Control System. A pressure chamber is connected to an infinite pressure source through a control valve. A measuring element senses the pressure in the chamber and sends a signal to a controller which actuates the control valve. A study is made of the response of the system to ramp and step changes in the gas flow rate leaving the pressure chamber. This requires 17 operational amplifiers (eight integrators), 19 pots, two servomultipliers, four diodes, two function switches, and 11 voltage supplies.

6. Simulation of a Reciprocating Gas Compressor. A cylinder-piston combination is described by three equations which express the change of cylinder pressure with time, the volumetric flow rate of intake gas, and the volumetric flow rate of exhaust gas, in terms of system parameters. Five simplifying assumptions are listed. The computer study requires 11 operational amplifiers (three integrators), ten pots, two servomultipliers, four diodes, and five voltage supplies.

7. This sheet gives pictorial symbols for PACE analog computer components.

8. Simulation of Antenna Radiation. The determination of the power radiation pattern for a half-wave dipole from a known current or field distribution over the surface of the antenna. The final computer diagram is given in block form, and seems to require four operational amplifiers (three integrators), four pots, two sine-cosine multipliers, two X^2 multipliers, a null sensor relay, two input voltage supplies, and an X-Y plotter.

PACE Application Bulletins. There are eight of these bulletins, which are reprints of articles and papers written on the title topics. The bulletins are rather detailed discussions of problems, followed by setups for analog solution. These bulletins may be obtained upon request from Electronic Associates, Inc., Long Branch, New Jersey.

1. Steam-Jacketed Kettle with Cascade Control System. The system is broken down into several subsystems, and each of these is simulated on the computer.

(a) Jacketed kettle. This requires three operational amplifiers (all integrators), 13 pots, and four voltage supplies.

(b) Simulation of control valve flow rates. This requires four operational amplifiers (no integrators), ten pots, two servo-multipliers, four diodes, and six voltage supplies.

(c) Simulation of valve turbulence factor for input of water jacket temperature transmitter. This requires three operational amplifiers (no integrators), three pots, the same two servomultipliers as in (b) above, and one voltage supply.

(d) Simulation of batch temperature transmitter. Four operational amplifiers (two integrators), seven pots, one diode, and two voltage supplies are required.

(e) Simulation of jacket-water temperature transmitter. This requires three operational amplifiers (all integrators), one pot, one servomultiplier, and one voltage supply.

(f) There are two controllers in the control system. The simulation of the proportional-integral controller requires four operational amplifiers (one integrator), four pots, two diodes, and two voltage supplies. The compensated derivative controller requires three operational amplifiers (one integrator), two pots, two diodes, and one voltage supply.

2. Application Bulletin No. 2 is not available.

3.. Analog Computers in Process Design. This bulletin gives circuits for simulation of several control system devices and responses.

(a) Spring-loaded, pneumatically operated control valve motor. This requires three operational amplifiers (two integrators), three pots, and will require up to two voltage supplies if two initial conditions are used.

(b) Theoretical proportional-integral controller. This requires four operational amplifiers (one integrator), three pots, and one voltage supply.

(c) Simulation of valve characteristics. One servo function generator is required.

(d) Simulation of jacketed thermocouple (two constants in system). This requires two integrators and four pots.

(e) Simulation of the nth section of a heat exchanger. This requires three operational amplifiers (one integrator), two pots, two servomultipliers, and two voltage supplies.

(f) Material balance for bottom plate of a distillation column. This requires one integrator, one pot, one servomultiplier, and two voltage supplies.

(g) Simulation of a first-order chemical reaction. This requires four operational amplifiers (one integrator), three pots, three multipliers, and one voltage supply.

(h) Simple model of a catalytic reactor (a simplified form of Wehner and Wilhelm's model, see Simulation Bulletin No. 4). This requires two integrators, four pots, and two voltage supplies.

4. Analog Computer Solution of Chemical Reactor Problems. This bulletin leaves something to be desired in clarity. Standard symbols are not used in the computer diagrams. A batch reactor problem is presented, and it seems to require eight operational amplifiers (three integrators), ten pots, three servomultipliers, and four voltage supplies. Another problem is presented on heterocontinuous reactors. This requires ten operational amplifiers (eight integrators), 30 pots, two diode function generators, two servomultipliers, and eight voltage supplies.

5. An Analog Computer Study of the Stability of a Molten-Zone Refining Process Used in the Production of Transistors. Equations are developed for determining the surface of revolution

of a hanging liquid drop as a function of the x and y dimensions of the drop and the length of the drop, h. The computer solution requires that the problem be run with x as the independent variable to obtain the boundary conditions for the initial conditions of the second part of the solution, where the problem is run with y as the independent variable. The computer circuit for generating h requires three operational amplifiers (no integrators), two pots, one servomultiplier, and a DPDT relay. The circuit for the solution of the portion where x is the independent variable requires eleven operational amplifiers (three integrators), nine pots, four servomultipliers, a DPDT relay, a DPST relay, and six voltage supplies. For the second part, where y is the independent variable, there are required ten operational amplifiers (three integrators), eight pots, four servomultipliers, and six voltage supplies.

6. Dynamic Analysis of an Aircraft Arresting Gear System. A discussion of the response of an arresting gear system for the recovery of naval aircraft on land where runway lengths are at a premium. The system consists of a cable restrained at each end by a movable mass and a piston. Equations are developed and the computer simulations shown for the problem. The piston computer circuit requires seven operational amplifiers (two integrators), two pots, a servomultiplier, a curve follower function generator, and a DPST switch. The carriage (mass) computer circuit requires five operational amplifiers (two integrators), two pots, and a DPST switch. The aircraft and kinematic circuit require seven operational amplifiers (two integrators), three pots, three servomultipliers, and two voltage supplies.

7. Simulation of a Reciprocating Compressor. A study of the behavior of the analog simulation of a reciprocating compressor with its associated piping. A more detailed study than that found in PACE Simulation Bulletin No. 6, discussed previously. The problem analysis and development of equations are given, followed by the computer diagrams. Simulation of the cylinder and valving requires 14 operational amplifiers (three integrators), 12 pots, seven diodes, two DPST relays, three electronic multipliers, three servomultipliers, an X^2 diode function generator, and five voltage supplies. The crank motion simulator requires 12 operational

amplifiers (two integrators), 15 pots, three servomultipliers, and five voltage supplies. The pipe section simulator (lumped-parameter representation) requires three operational amplifiers (two integrators), four pots, and one voltage supply.

8. Application Bulletin No. 8 is not available.

9. A Method of Solving the Steady-State Equation of an Ammonia Synthesis Process. A computer circuit is developed which computes the liquid ammonia yield of the process as a function of the purge valve openings. A large computer is required for this problem, since, for instance, 59 operational amplifiers are required. The required computer components for the solution will not be given. The reader who has access to computing equipment of this size is referred to the Bulletin.

10. Plotting Results of a Quadratic Regression Analysis. A description of a generalized analog computer program for plotting the results of a quadratic regression equation with four independent variables. A large computer is required. The interested reader is referred to the bulletin.

"Analog Computer Applications in the Chemical and Petroleum Industries," a seminar presented by Electronics Associates, Inc., Long Branch, New Jersey.

This booklet, available without charge from EAI, contains discussions of the general purpose electronic analog computer and the use of the computer. There follow nine applications of the computer to steady-state and unsteady-state design problems, and several problems on process control systems. These applications are discussed below.

1. Tubular Reactor Design. Four pages. The same problem as that given in Simulation Bulletin No. 3, described previously. The Simulation Bulletin gives almost no discussion, but does give a computer circuit and numerical values for computer settings. The booklet currently being discussed gives a fairly detailed equation derivation and the computer circuit, but no computer settings.

2. Design of a Cooler-Condenser. Four pages. A calculation of the required heat transfer area of a cooler-condenser for various operating conditions. This requires 17 operational amplifiers (two

integrators), 20 pots, four diode function generators, ten electronic multipliers, four DPST relays, and eight voltage supplies.

3. Design of an Ethylene Process. Five pages. A preliminary evaluation of a semi-works plant for the cracking of hydrocarbons to acetylene and ethylene. The process to be used is described in Akin, G. A., T. F. Reid, and R. J. Schrader, *Chemical Engineering Progress*, **54**, (1958) 41. The complete computer diagram is not given, but the essential parts are shown. The circuit for calculating the theoretical flame temperature requires one integrating amplifier, two function multipliers, and a diode function generator. The generation of partial pressure requires two operational amplifiers (one integrator), one pot, two servomultipliers, and a voltage supply. Generation of the specific reaction rate, using the Arrhenius equation, requires three operational amplifiers, two pots, two log x fixed diode function generators, a servo function generator, a servomultiplier, and one voltage supply.

4. Multi-Component Distillation Column. Five pages. A calculation of the component compositions of a multi-component distillation as a function of column plates, for various operating conditions. This development is applicable to calculations from the bottom plate to the feed plate. The computer diagrams are not self-explanatory, but the following equipment seems to be necessary. For each component, the component material balance is used to calculate the liquid rate. This requires (per component, evidently) six operational amplifiers (no integrators), three pots, a function switch, two servomultipliers, three servo function generators, and a voltage supply. Bottoms flow rate is calculated from the heat balance equation, which requires three operational amplifiers (one integrator), three pots, a servomultiplier, and two voltage supplies. Vapor flow rate is calculated from the over-all material balance equation, and requires an operational amplifier and a servomultiplier. The plate temperature calculation requires an integrator, a pot, and a servomultiplier.

5. Investigation of Reaction Kinetics. Four pages. A pilot plant uses a complicated feed with a number of components. The reactions are not known, but are believed to be complicated. Pilot plant data give component composition as a function of

reactor length for isothermal operation. The analog computer is to be used to try to find the mechanism. This requires five operational amplifiers (two integrators), three pots, two servomultipliers, and three voltage supplies.

6. Investigation of the Transient Behavior of a Semi-Batch Reactor Process. Five pages. A reactor has continuous feed, no withdrawal of product, and complete mixing. The reversible reaction occurring is $A + B$ going to $C + D$. The computer is used to investigate the time responses of reactor concentrations, temperatures, rates, and volume changes. The calculation of each of the two reaction rates requires an operational amplifier, two pots, a log x diode function generator, and a voltage supply. Generation of the reactor concentrations requires 12 operational amplifiers (four integrators), six pots, six servomultipliers, and one voltage supply. The calculation of reaction volume involves two operational amplifiers (one integrator), two pots, two servomultipliers (one of which is also involved in the reactor concentration circuit), and two voltage supplies. Solution of the heat balance equation requires eight operational amplifiers (one integrator), seven pots, two servomultipliers, and four voltage supplies.

7. Transient Study of a Packed Column. Four pages. A study of the transient performance of a packed column utilizing two fluid streams, countercurrent operation. There is a brief discussion of pertinent equations and a very sketchy discussion of computer programming. A circuit is shown only for the concentration of liquid with time in the rth section. This circuit requires four operational amplifiers (one integrator), three pots, one servomultiplier, and one voltage supply.

8. Investigation of the Process Parameters Affecting the Control of a Stirred-Tank Reactor. Two pages. The same problem as that discussed in PACE Application Note No. 10. The Application Note gives the better treatment.

9. Representation of a Heat Exchanger on an Analog Computer. Two pages. An investigation of the dynamic performance of a countercurrent heat enchanger for use in an atomic reactor power system. A circuit is shown for simulation of the $m + 3/2$ station of the heat exchanger. This circuit requires six operational amplifiers

(three integrators), 11 pots, and one voltage supply. The heat transfer parameters were assumed constant; if they are assumed to be dependent upon fluid flow rate and temperature, nonlinear equipment will have to be added.

10. The Use of the Electronic Analog Computer for the Solution of Process Control Problems. Seven pages. This is very nearly the same material as that covered in PACE Application Bulletin No. 3, discussed previously. Circuits given which were not given in Application Bulletin No. 3 are outlined here.

(a) Thermocouple without protecting bulb. This requires one integrator and two pots.

(b) Filled thermal system with transport delay. This requires four operational amplifiers (three integrators), five pots, and an input voltage.

(c) Simulation of density and specific gravity meters, flow and level instruments which measure from a pressure differential, and mechanical instruments. This requires three operational amplifiers (two integrators), four pots, and a voltage input.

(d) Proportional controller. This requires one operational amplifier, one pot, and a voltage supply.

(e) Proportional-speed floating controller. This requires two operational amplifiers (one integrator), one pot, and a voltage supply.

(f) Proportional plus compensated derivative controller. This requires four operational amplifiers (one integrator), one pot, and a voltage supply.

Field, William B., "Design of a pH Control System by Analog Simulation," *ISA Journal*, 6, (1959). A reprint of this article is available without charge from Electronic Associates, Inc.

A discussion, without mathematics, of a computer study of the title subject. A computer diagram is shown for one of the blenders with its associated control mechanisms, and another condensed schematic shows the process interaction of all three blenders and the two associated control systems. The first computer circuit requires: (a) for the mixer, two operational amplifiers (one integrator), and one servomultiplier; (b) for the transport delay, the same; (c) for the measurement device, the same; (d) for the three-mode controller, five operational amplifiers (one integrator), four pots, and a voltage supply; (e) for the valve, one integrator, three pots, two diodes, and two voltage supplies.

The condensed schematic for the entire system requires combination of two of the above computer circuits with certain other equipment. The interested reader is referred to the article.

Worley, Charles W., "Simulation of A Liquid Level Control System," Volume I in a series of Analog Computer Applications. A reprint is available from Electronic Associates, Inc. 12 pages.

The system studied is a single-tank liquid level process in which the liquid head is controlled by manipulation of a pneumatic valve in the outflow stream upon command of a proportional-integral controller. The problem is discussed, equations are developed, and computer circuits are shown for the following four parts of the system: (a) the liquid level process, which requires three operational amplifiers (one integrator), three pots, a servomultiplier (to handle the nonlinear tank outflow resistance), and one voltage supply; (b) the measuring element, a differential pressure transmitter, which requires three operational amplifiers (two integrators) and four pots; (c) the proportional-integral controller, which is represented by four operational amplifiers (one integrator), four pots, two diodes, and two voltage supplies; and (d) the control valve, which requires two integrators and four pots.

Katz, Donald L., and Elliot I. Organick. *Integration of Electronic Computers into the Undergraduate Engineering Educational Program.* First Annual Report of the Ford Foundation Project, College of Engineering, University of Michigan, Ann Arbor, Michigan (1960).

1. Mass-Spring-Damper System (pp. 477–480). Two circuits are shown for solution of the problem. The easiest for the beginner to comprehend requires four operational amplifiers (two integrators) and a maximum of two voltage supplies. Good discussion accompanies problem.

2. Two-Degree of Freedom System (pp. 480–482). A vibrating system consisting of two masses and three springs. This requires six

operational amplifiers (four integrators) with a maximum of four voltage supplies. Good discussion accompanies problem.

3. Same problem as Number (1) above, but with potentiometers added to allow rapid variation of constant coefficients in equation (pp. 483–492). It requires the addition of three pots to the component list of Number (1). This problem is used as the example to explain time and magnitude scaling.

4. Simplified Automobile Suspension System (pp. 493–497). The suspension of one automobile tire is simulated by two masses, two springs, and a shock absorber (dashpot). The circuit requires eight operational amplifiers (four integrators), five pots, and up to four voltage supplies. If the viscous damping constant is to be made a nonlinear function of the velocity, add a diode function generator. Good discussion accompanies problem.

5. The Equation of Heat Flow (pp. 497–504). A determination of the temperature in an infinite slab as a function of distance through the slab and time. Solution by separation of variables gives an eigenvalue problem, the circuit requiring four operational amplifiers (three integrators), four pots, a function generator, a function multiplier, and no more than three voltage supplies. If the partial differential equation is solved by finite-difference techniques, the circuit requires 18 operational amplifiers (six integrators), 12 pots, and up to six voltage supplies. This is for six active temperature stations distributed throughout the slab. The discussion accompanying the problem is good.

6. The Van der Pol Equation (pp. 505–508). This equation represents the behavior of certain electronic oscillator circuits. The equation is presented and discussed, and scaling of the problem for computer solution is also discussed. The computer circuit requires five operational amplifiers (two integrators), four pots, two multipliers, and no more than three voltage supplies.

7. Solution of Nonlinear Electrical Circuits (pp. 513–515). This problem involves an *RLC* circuit with a nonlinear inductance. The input to the system is a square wave. The problem is intended to impress upon the student the fact that in a nonlinear circuit the possibility exists of the generation of harmonics and subharmonics. The computer circuit requires four operational amplifiers (two

integrators), two diodes (semiconductor), one Zener diode, three pots, and two voltage supplies.

8. Transient Analysis of an *RLC* Circuit with Sinusoidal Excitation (pp. 516–519). The instantaneous values of circuit current and capacitor charge are to be determined. The circuit requires six operational amplifiers (four integrators), four pots, and four voltage supplies (the sinusoidal forcing function is generated on the computer).

9. Transient Behavior of Batch Reactor System (pp. 524, 531–535). A study of reactions occurring in a batch reactor with constant-volume, isothermal conditions. Analog computer studies are shown for (1), the reversible reaction *A* going to *B*, and (2), the reversible reaction *A* going to *B* going to *C*. (1) requires two integrators, two pots, and up to two voltage supplies. (2) requires three integrators, four pots, and up to three voltage supplies.

10. Oxygen Depletion in Streams (pp. 536–538). A study of the predicted course of the oxygen assets of a stream under the combined influence of deoxygenation resulting from pollution, and reaeration following the establishment of an oxygen deficit. The circuit requires four operational amplifiers (two integrators), two pots, and up to two voltage supplies.

Nichols, M. H., and D. W. Hagelbarger, "A Simple Electronic Differential Analyzer as a Demonstration and Laboratory Aid to Instruction in Engineering," report by the Department of Aeronautical Engineering, University of Michigan, Ann Arbor (1951).

1. Mass-Spring-Damper System with One Degree of Freedom (pp. 11–17). Two computer circuits are shown, the more complicated of which requires four operational amplifiers (two integrators) three pots, and no more than two voltage supplies. Good discussion accompanies problem.

2. Spring-Mass System with Dry Friction (p. 18). Introduction of a nonlinearity by substituting a dry friction damper for the viscous damper of Problem (1). This requires six operational amplifiers (two integrators), three pots, and up to two voltage sources. Short discussion.

3. Servomechanisms (pp. 18–25). A study of a servomecha-

nism with viscous output damping, error rate damping, and integral control. The circuit requires eight operational amplifiers (four integrators), six pots, an SPST switch, and no more than four voltage supplies. A good discussion accompanies the problem.

4. Coupled Systems—The Dynamic Vibration Absorber (pp. 25–27). Response of the system to a sinusoidal forcing function. The circuit requires eight operational amplifiers (four integrators), nine pots, and no more than four voltage supplies. The sine wave is generated separately. A short discussion accompanies the problem.

5. Boundary Value Problems—The Thin Uniform Beam with Static Uniform Load (pp. 25, 28–33). Circuits are given for solution of the problem with both ends hinged, and with both beam ends free. For the hinged-hinged beam, there are required four integrators, one pot, and two voltage supplies. The free-free beam requires the same equipment. Good discussion given.

6. Consecutive Chemical Reactions (pp. 34–45). The problem involves the first-order unimolecular chemical reaction A going to B going to C going to D. Four integrators, six pots, and no more than four voltage supplies are required. Short discussion given.

Wheeler, R. C. H., and G. F. Kinney, "Programming Chemical Kinetics Problems for Electronic Analogue Computers," *Transactions of the IRE*. Professional Group on Industrial Electronics, PGIE-3 (March, 1956) 70.

1. Simple Radioactive Decay. Decay of Na^{24} to Mg^{24} by electron emission. The circuit requires one integrator, two pots, and a voltage supply.

2. Consecutive Reactions. First-order unidirectional reactions of the type X going to Y going to Z, illustrated by Zr^{95} going to Cb^{95} going to Mo^{95}. The circuit requires three integrators, four pots, and no more than three voltage supplies (one would be most common). If one wants only the amounts of Zr^{95} and Cb^{95} with time, and the total radioactivity with time, then the circuit requires four operational amplifiers (two integrators), six pots, and one voltage supply.

3. Complex Reactions. First-order reaction of A reversibly forming A^*, the activated complex. Then A^* goes unidirectionally to B. The circuit requires three integrators, five pots, and a voltage supply.

Each problem is accompanied by a good discussion, and the recorded results are shown for each computer.

Williams, T. J., "The Operation of the Analog Computer and its use in Investigating Chemical Process Dynamics," house manual on analog computation published by Monsanto Chemical Company, Research and Engineering Division, 800 North Lindbergh Boulevard, St. Louis, Missouri.

This manual contains a variety of illustrative computer circuits, all of which will not be noted. The following are some of those given.

1. Generation of At^2 (p. 118). This requires two integrators, one pot, and a voltage supply.

2. Generation of $V_0 \sin \omega t$ or $V_0 \cos \omega t$ (p. 119). Three operational amplifiers (two integrators), three pots, and a voltage supply are required.

3. Generation of $E_0 e^{-kt}$ (p. 119). This requires one integrator, one pot, and a voltage supply.

4. Generation of $E_0 e^{+kt}$ (p. 119). This requires two operational amplifiers (one integrator), one pot, and a voltage supply.

5. Division to produce $10/t$ (p. 120). One operational amplifier, one pot, a servomultiplier, and a voltage supply are needed.

6. Generation of kx^3 (p. 121). This requires five operational amplifiers, one servomultiplier.

7. Generation of e^x (p. 121). This requires two operational amplifiers (one integrator), a servomultiplier, and a voltage supply.

8. Generation of $ky^{0.5}$ (p. 122). One operational amplifier, a servomultiplier, and a voltage supply are required.

9. Simple Limiting Circuit (p. 131). This requires one operational amplifier, two pots, two diodes, and three voltage supplies. A discussion is included.

10. Soft Limiting Circuit (p. 132). This requires the same components as (9), plus two resistors. A discussion is included.

11. Hard Limiting Circuit (p. 133). Three operational amplifiers, two pots, four diodes, and two voltage supplies are required. A circuit is also shown for accomplishing the same thing with relays instead of diodes. A discussion is included.

12. Hysteresis and Gear Backlash Circuit (pp. 134–136). This

requires three operational amplifiers, two diodes, one capacitor, and two voltage supplies. Another circuit is shown which uses relays instead of diodes. A discussion is included.

13. Dead Space Circuits (pp. 136–137). Two circuits are shown, the better one requiring three operational amplifiers, two pots, four diodes, and two voltage supplies. A discussion is included.

14. Static Friction Circuits (pp. 136–138). Two circuits are given, one using diodes and the other using relays. The diode circuit requires one operational amplifier, two pots, two diodes, and two voltage supplies. A discussion is included.

15. Absolute Value Circuits (pp. 140–141). Two circuits given, the more complicated of which requires four operational amplifiers, two pots, four diodes, and two voltage supplies.

16. Transport Delay Circuits (pp. 141–146). Generation of e^{-Ts} by expanding it in an infinite series. Circuits are given for a first order approximation, a second order approximation, and a fourth order approximation. The last circuit requires six operational amplifiers (four integrators), 12 pots, and a voltage supply. A discussion is included.

17. On pages 293–309, the first six Simulation Bulletins issued by Electronics Associates, Inc., are reproduced. These have already been reviewed here.

Williams, T. J., *et al.* "Analog Computer Demonstration Problems." A 67-page report by the Systems Engineering Section of Monsanto Chemical Company, June, 1960. All problems have good accompanying discussions.

1. A Study of the Effects of Various Frequencies of Oscillation and Damping Factors on a General Second-Order Differential Equation (pp. 3–4). A phase plane analysis is made. The circuit requires four operational amplifiers (two integrators), five pots, and two voltage supplies.

2. Tuned Torsional Pendulum (pp. 5–8). A study of a tuned torsional pendulum for various damping factors. The circuit requires six operational amplifiers (four integrators), ten pots, and four voltage supplies.

3. The Low-Velocity Spherical Cannon Ball (pp. 9–12). A computer study of a ballistic trajectory problem. The circuit requires four integrators, eight pots, and two voltage supplies.

4. A Monkey on a Unicycle (pp. 13–16). A chimpanzee is to ride a unicycle in the Forest Park Zoo Circus. The problem involves the design of a smooth-riding unicycle for the performer, assuming the tire has an equivalent spring constant and the seat has a combination spring-damper effect. Nine operational amplifiers (four integrators), ten pots, and up to four voltage supplies are needed.

5. Hand-Fired Short Range Missile Simulator (pp. 17–20). The construction of an analog missile simulator for training of firing officers. The missile will be fired in two phases: Phase I will be fired straight up to acquire altitude; Phase II is programmed to fire at some previously determined altitude and at some previously determined angle of attack. The thrust is fixed, but the angle of attack may be varied, and the firing officer controls the time of firing for Phase II. Five integrators, eight pots, two switches (DPST), and one voltage supply are required.

6. Long-Range Ballistic Missile (pp. 21–24). The determination of the point of impact of a two-stage missile for various firing times. The thrust is fixed, while the angle of attack of Stage II and burning times for both stages are variable. This requires nine operational amplifiers (five integrators), 14 pots, one servo multiplier, five switches (appear to be relay switches), and nine voltage supplies (all 100-volt).

7. Gas Dynamics of a Compressor (pp. 25–28). A computer solution of the P-V diagram of a gas compressor is required for analysis. Various conditions of pressure and volume are to be studied. This requires eight operational amplifiers (three integrators), seven pots, two servomultipliers, three switches (appear to be relay switches), and five voltage supplies.

8. Simulation of a Bouncing Ball (pp. 29–32). A study of the bouncing ball, including various initial velocities and various ball hardnesses. This requires six operational amplifiers (four integrators), seven pots, four switches (appear to be relay switches), and five voltage supplies.

9. Transient Study of a Heat Process (pp. 34–37). A study of

the transient response of a jacketed kettle to determine the effect of flow changes and inlet temperature changes upon the process temperature. Nine operational amplifiers (three integrators), 11 pots, and five voltage supplies are needed.

10. Control of a Heat Transfer Process (pp. 38–42). Control of the output temperature of the jacketed kettle of Problem (9). The controller is a proportional-integral type. Nineteen operational amplifiers (five integrators), 18 pots, a servomultiplier, and nine voltage supplies are required.

11. Control of a Reaction Process (pp. 43–46). The determination of the proper controller settings (proportional-integral) for maintaining a constant output composition level in a chemical reactor which is subjected to imposed upsets in the rate of input of reactants. Chemical reaction is $A + B \rightarrow 2C$. This requires 14 operational amplifiers (five integrators), 13 pots, one diode, two servomultipliers, and eight voltage supplies.

12. High-Speed Adaptive Control System (pp. 47–50). A servomechanism is to be designed to have stated requirements. A simulation is developed to study the system before money is appropriated for its manufacture. The study involves using the computer to plot phase planes. This requires five operational amplifiers (two integrators), six pots, five switches (relay switches?), a control switch having RESET, HOLD, and OPERATE positions, and six voltage supplies.

13. Control of a Simple Single-Pass Heat Exchanger (pp. 51–54). Single-pass, concentric tube heat exchanger, with coolant in annulus. The tube outlet temperature will be controlled by varying the shell flow rate. The controller utilizes proportional-derivative action. Twelve operational amplifiers (five integrators), 21 pots, one servomultiplier, four time relays, and 12 voltage supplies are required.

14. Chlorination of Benzene (pp. 56–58). A study of the kinetics of a batch reactor for the chlorination of benzene. Three reactions go forward simultaneously, with kinetic coefficients given. This requires eight operational amplifiers (five integrators), five pots, and two voltage supplies.

15. Chemical Kinetics (pp. 60–63). First-order irreversible

reactions as follows:

$$A + B \xrightarrow{k_1} 2C$$

$$B + C \xrightarrow{k_2} 2D$$

$$D \xrightarrow{k_3} E.$$

The kinetic coefficients are given, and it is desired to investigate the concentrations of the reactants and products with time. Eleven operational amplifiers (six integrators), six pots, one servomultiplier and three voltage supplies are needed.

16. Catalytic Isothermal Dehydrogenation (pp. 64–67). Three principal reactions represent the catalytic isothermal dehydrogenation of an aromatic compound, as follows:

$$A \rightleftarrows B + H_2$$

$$A + H_2 \rightarrow C + C_2H_6$$

$$A + H_2 \rightarrow D + CH_4.$$

It is desired to observe the variation of the moles of B, C, and D with time. This requires 12 operational amplifiers (three integrators), eight pots, two servomultipliers, and three voltage supplies. There are some other notations on the computer diagram which this writer does not understand, but which may represent time-controlled relays. An X-Y plotter can be used to write out the answer, in which case add one integrator, one pot, and a voltage supply.

Yeager, Robert L., "The Analog Computer," *Military Automation*, **1**, (March-April, 1957). A reprint is available from Electronic Associates, Inc.

Brief discussions of several computer applications, with final computer circuits shown.

1. Analysis of a Servomechanism. A continuous closed-loop positioning system is discussed in which the error between desired and actual shaft position is amplified and applied to the field winding of a d-c servo motor. This requires five operational amplifiers (three integrators), four pots, and an input voltage representing the desired shaft position.

2. Seat Ejection Study. Design of a seat ejection system, for a high-speed jet aircraft, which will assure the pilot's safe removal from the plane. A ballistic charge plus a small rocket motor furnishes the motive power. Two portions of the problem are discussed and the circuit diagrams shown. The first determines the propellant grain burning surface as a function of the linear percentage burned, and requires one operational amplifier, three pots, a function multiplier, and a voltage supply. The second is a force balance within the tube supporting the ejection seat (which also contains the ballistic charge and the rocket motor) to determine the stroke required. This circuit uses five operational amplifiers (two integrators), three pots, a diode function generator, and a voltage supply.

Bibliography

[1] JACKSON, ALBERT S. *Analog Computation.* New York: McGraw-Hill Book Co., Inc., 1960. Pp. 297–352.

[2] ROGERS, A. E., and T. W. CONNOLLY. *Analog Computation in Engineering Design.* New York: McGraw-Hill Book Co., Inc., 1960. Pp. 158–216.

[3] MIDDENDORF, WILLIAM H. *Analysis of Electric Circuits.* New York: John Wiley and Sons, 1956. Pp. 35–42.

[4] VAN VALKENBURG, M. E. *Network Analysis.* Englewood Cliffs, N. J.: Prentice-Hall, 1955. Pp. 125–147, 194–211.

[5] GRAY, TRUMAN S. *Applied Electronics,* 2d ed. New York: John Wiley and Sons, 1954. Pp. 390–416.

[6] THE INSTITUTE OF RADIO ENGINEERS. *Standards on Abbreviations, Graphical Symbols, Letter Symbols, and Mathematical Signs.* New York: The Institute of Radio Engineers, 1948. Pp. 2–3.

[7] GRAY, *op. cit.,* Pp. 405–408.

[8] RAGAZZINI, JOHN R., ROBERT H. RANDALL, and FREDERICK A. RUSSELL. "Analysis of Problems in Dynamics by Electronic Circuits," *Proc. IRE,* **35** (May, 1947) 445–452.

[9] GRABBE, EUGENE G., SIMON RAMO, and DEAN E. WOOLDRIDGE. *Handbook of Automation, Computation, and Control,* Vol. 2. New York: John Wiley and Sons, 1959. Chapter 22, p. 31.

[10] GRAY, *op. cit.,* Pp. 492–494.

[11] THE HEATH COMPANY. "Assembling and Using Your Heathkit D-C Amplifier, Model ES-201." Benton Harbor: The Heath Co., 1959. Pp. 3–4.

[12] THE HEATH COMPANY. "Operational Manual for the Educational Electronic Analog Computer, Model EC-1." Benton Harbor: The Heath Co., 1962. P. 35.

[13] WASS, C. A. A. *Introduction to Electronic Analogue Computers.* (Electronics and Waves Series, D. W. Fry, ed.). New York and London: Pergamon Press, 1956. Pp. 96–97.

[14] KORN, GRANINO A., and THERESA M. KORN. *Electronic Analog Computers,* 2d ed. New York: McGraw-Hill Book Co., Inc., 1956. P. 239.

[15] JOHNSON, CLARENCE L., *Analog Computer Techniques.* New York: McGraw-Hill Book Co., Inc., 1956. Pp. 184–189.

[16] KORN and KORN, *op. cit.,* pp. 191–196, 231–248.

[17] WASS, *op. cit.,* pp. 76–89.

[18] JACKSON, *op. cit.,* pp. 145–148.

[19] BRYANT, LAWRENCE T., LOUIS C. JUST, and GERARD S. PAWLICKI. *Introduction to Electronic Analogue Computing.* Argonne: Report ANL-6187, Argonne National Laboratory, 1960. Pp. 20–23.

[20] JOHNSON, *op. cit.,* pp. 66–69.

[21] WASS, *op. cit.,* pp. 111–119.

[22] JOHNSON, *op. cit.,* pp. 137–141.

[23] WASS, *op. cit.,* pp. 124–128.

[24] JOHNSON, *op. cit.,* pp. 69–77.

[25] JACKSON, *op. cit.,* pp. 485–492.

[26] KORN and KORN, *op. cit.,* pp. 290–299.

[27] JOHNSON, *op. cit.,* pp. 153–157.

[28] *Ibid.,* p. 24.

[29] *Ibid.,* p. 25.

[30] *Ibid.,* p. 33.

[31] JACKSON, *op cit.,* pp. 26–28, 99–100.

[32] *Ibid.,* pp. 101–103.

[33] VAN VALKENBURG, *op. cit.,* pp. 415–417.

Index

ABOUT THE AUTHORS

JAMES EDWARD STICE is Associate Professor of Chemical Engineering at the University of Arkansas. He received his MS and PhD degrees in 1952 and 1963, respectively, from the Illinois Institute of Technology.

While obtaining his MS, Professor Stice attended the Institute as an Armour Research Foundation Fellow, and while working on his PhD he was also an Instructor in the Chemical Engineering Department and later became a National Science Foundation Faculty Fellow at the same school.

His professional affiliations include American Institute of Chemical Engineering, American Society for Engineering Education, Instrument Society of America and the American Association for the Advancement of Science.

BERNET S. SWANSON is Professor of Chemical Engineering at the Illinois Institute of Technology where he has taught since 1947. Professor Swanson received his MS at the Institute in 1944 and his PhD from the same school in 1950.

The author's special fields of interest are instrumentation and control, process dynamics and computer control. He has worked in a consulting capacity for the Atomic Energy Commission, the National Science Foundation and various valve and instrument manufacturers.

Professor Swanson is a member of the American Institute of Chemical Engineering and has served on the education projects committee, automatic control committee and the machine computation committee.

THIS BOOK WAS SET IN

TIMES ROMAN AND BULMER TYPES

BY TRADE COMPOSITION, INC.

IT WAS DESIGNED BY THE STAFF OF

BLAISDELL PUBLISHING COMPANY